THE REMARKABLE SAGA OF

OLE & LENA

THE REMARKABLE SAGA OF
SAGA OF
OLE & LENA

Written And Illustrated

By Richard Thorud

Elliot House

Bloomington, Minnesota

Library of Congress No. Catalog Card No: 99-96851
Thorud, Richard A.
    The Remarkable Saga of Ole and Lena, First Edition

ISBN 0-9675454-0-4

Published by: Elliot House
               10030 Elliot Ave. So.
               Bloomington, Minnesota, 55420

Printed and bound in the United States of America.
First printing 1999.

To my wife, Darlene,
whose total disinterest in my work
keeps me humble.

Table of Contents

Acknowledgements

I wish to thank the following people, who took time to read and critique the manuscript for this book at various times during its development—

Darlene Thorud
Michael Thorud
Lori Thorud
Ardelle Thorud
Bruce Nord
Roger Nelson

Preface

Everyone's heard about Ole and Lena, of course. Them two is far and away the best known Skandinavians there ever wuz. One time or other we've all chuckled over some a' them outrageous Ole and Lena jokes that's always makin' the rounds. But hey—did yew ever stop and ask yerself, "Just who wuz them two, really?" And if yew did, deep down yew surely knew there's no place with an answer. Well, at last there's a well-written, scholarly book to fill that void—

and yew got it in yer hands right now, by golly!

Part One deals with Ole. Some folks say he's kinduva Swedish Paul Bunyan, him bein' such a legendary, larger-than-life feller. We'll be taggin' along as Ole stumbles through a whole mess of adventurous fiascos, first in Sweden and then in Amerika. Ole's got his critics, a' course. They say the big galoot's as dumb as he is smart, and as awkward as he is athletic—

and I guess that's probably true, the more yew think about it.

Ole's likable enough. He means well, and he's innocent as a new-born lamb. But he has this one big problem— namely, that bad luck seems t' follow him wherever he goes.

Then in Part Two we meet Lena, who is sorta the Norwegian version of a Paulette Bunyan, I guess. She's got critics galore (includin' me), and I've heard her described as a fat, fudge-brained, free-spirited floozie—all of which is true. The truth is that Lena's just the opposite of Ole. In fact, she's a flat-out embarrassment t' write about, her bein' such a wild and loose-livin' party animal. I'd just as soon leave her out of this book—

but then yew can't have Ole without Lena!

Lena's utter lack of caution is as legendary as her utter lack of brains. And speakin' of legends, I should mention that Lena's also a legendary Norse beauty, somehow, despite her ample abundance of excess flesh. Indeed— this lady completely fills the spotlight wherever she goes. And like Ole, she too has a whole hotdish of fast-paced adventures—

even though most of hers is best forgot!

Lastly, Part Three tells how Ole and Lena finally meet and get married. And though this concludes our book, it's not really the end a' the story—cuz this is where all them Ole and Lena jokes take over. Of course, yew know that some of them jokes are—shall we say—a bit "off-color." But rest assured that this here book is the hand-scrubbed "G-rated" family edition, suitable fer Skandinavians of all ages—at least fer those of yew who can read. And it's profusely illustrated too, in case yew ain't too good at picturin' things in yer head.

Lastly, yew should know that this book comes highly rekommended, mostly by the author hisself. In fact, he suggests that yew buy two—one to read, and one to tuck away, cuz it's bound t' be a hot collectible!

Yew betcha!

Richard A. Thorud
Bloomington, Minnesota
1999

PART ONE:
BIG OLE

THE GREAT
SWEDE INVENTOR

Ole Oscar Svensson
A Legend In His Own Time

Chapter One:
In The Beginning

Ole Gets Born

Well, those of yew who want to know all about Big Ole and Little Lena have got the right book, by golly! Yer about to learn whatever there is t' know about 'em, both fact and legend. But before delvin' into the legend part, let's start with the known facts first.

It seems that Ole wuz a substantial tot right frum day one. He weighed 44 lb. 4 oz. comin' out, and by the time his ma rekovered he'd gained 12 more. As with most Swedes, it wuz slow goin' at first. Ole remained a diapered, breast-fed babe fer nigh onto 9 years, at which time he learned to walk and talk. But then he hit a growth spurt in both brain and body, and when he first enrolled in school (at age 14), he wuz the largest—if not the smartest—first-grader in Swedish hist'ry, weighin' in at 192.2 pounds.

So yew kin see that Ole wuz a downright exceptional young lad—*even by Swedish standards!*

Ole Goes To School

Ole did real good at school, espeshully in the 3 R's— which in Swedish schools wuz <u>R</u>uff-housin', <u>R</u>unnin' wild, and actin' <u>R</u>owdy. Hardly a day'd go by but whut he caused a stir. Take spellin' class, fer instance. Ole constantly amazed his teacher by findin' new ways t' spell words—*ways that she'd not never heard of!*

Ole, aged one day!

Author's Note: Originally this book wuz gonna have actual photographs, until my wife accidentally threw 'em out. These sketches duplicates all them photos as best as I can remember.

And in geografy class? Why, he'd convinced most ev'ryone that Sweden wuz akshully located near the South Pole, *until someone diskovered the globe wuz upside down.*

Whatever!

Anyways, yew folks kin see fer yerselves that Ole wuz blessed with more brains than he knew whut t' do with. Bein' 3 IQ points smarter than the average Svensson, he graduated first in his 1st grade class *(akshully meanin' that he wuz the first one out the door).*

And since he wuz 18 at the time, he then dropped out to work full time on his pa's farm—
(despite his pa's objections).

Pa's Letter

Now, before we go much further, there's somethin' else yew should know about Ole. It's on the subject of luck. The big Swede just didn't have any. And that's why his pa wuz so concerned about his helpin' out on the farm.

"Vell, it ain't dat my boy Ole iss lazy," wrote Pa to cousin Rasmus. "Fer shure, he got enthuzyazm too burn! An' dey say he's smart too. But—dang it all—dere's da axident ven he got da fields mixed up, and planted korn vere I yust planted oats da day before!"

"An' da vun ven he pounded in all da fence poles upside down, so's da barbed vire ended up underground!"

"An' da time ven all our cows got drowned ven he vas fordin' da kreek vit 'em—even dough da kreek vas yust 6 inches deep!"

"Bein' his pa, I mighta overlookt dem times, I s'ppose. But after Ole managed too burn down da house tree times in too veeks—vell—I knowed right den dat it vas high time he vent back too skool!"

Ole and Friend

Back home on the farm!

Once Ole saw that his lot in life wuz to further his learnin', he turned dead serious about it.

"My kare-free days iss done and gone," he announced. "I vill now take da bull by da horns, an' milk it dry! An' I vill crack dem books and polish dose apples—an' fer shure I vill study hardly, and mold myself intoo vun a' dem dere hi-falutin' ivory-tower intellektyools. Yew betcha, by golly!"

Higher Learnin'

Ole's mentor this time wuz Professor Cal Q. Lasseson, a somewhut decrepit old country school teacher who wuz also known as "Squirt," due to his passion fer chawin' and spittin'. Now, Squirt just happened to be Sweden's greatest math'matikal genius. And mainly, he wuz famous fer his ability to recite the entire Pythagorean Theorem backwards, while chewin' a full box a' Copenhagen at the same time.[1]

Well—since Ole wuz so darn smart, Squirt chose to teach him higher math'matiks, which—akshully—wuz the same as regular math'matiks, *except it wuz taught on the second floor.*

Ole did real good in this class, partially cuz he could chaw and spit almost as good as Squirt hisself, but mainly cuz he could beat the old guy in arm wrestlin' 'most ev'ry time. Ole learned his math by doin' such things as countin' spits, and dividin' 'em into the number of arm wrestlin' heats. Once again, the big Swede graduated first in his class *(although this time, I guess he wuz the only one in his class).*

So then, regarding his math'matikal trainin', I guess that about *"sums it up."*

Whatever.

---

[1] Sweden's not exactly top-heavy on math'matikal geniuses, y' know.

Anyways—by the time Ole wuz full-growed, he stood 6 foot 6 inches tall, and weighed in at exactly 444 pounds. Some say he wuz slow-thinkin' and clumsy, but I don't say that.

I say he wuz a typical Swede!

And he wuz mainly a ruddy-skinned, clean-shaved, good-lookin' feller, with a carrot-colored mop a' top hair, and the strength of a 95th percentile Lapland musk ox. He wuz also the tobaccy-chewinist, bow-leggedist Swede who ever walked the face of planet earth. Truth is, if it warn't fer them bow-legs, the big galoot woulda topped 6 foot 10.

Yet—even though Ole had such awesome talents in that there math'matrickal stuff, he had trouble masterin' some of the simpler things in life.

- One thing wuz, he never did learn how t' lace his boots without lacin' 'em t'gether—

- And anuther thing wuz, he never did learn t' spit upwind successfully *(though he never did quit tryin')!*

Chapter Two:
Ole As A Young Man In Sweden

What's been said up 'til now is absolute fact fer shure. It's all in the hist'ry books. I shall now attempt to recount some of Ole's remarkable adventures in Sweden, frum the time before he went off to Amerika. But yew gotta realize, up front, that facts and such frum those early years is sorta scarce, plus it's startin' to git confounded with legend—and to tell the truth, some of it tends to git a little mixed up in my head.

Nonetheless, dear reader, with pen in hand I shall now present them old stories more accurate than is possible at this time. As a serious author and historian, I've tried really hard to weed out all the fiction—and I'm now 63 per cent shure that 100 per cent of most a' the stories included in this book is probably true. Indeed, they must be—the proof of it bein' that *truth is stranger than fiction!*

Ole And The Trolls

First off, there's the story of Ole and the trolls. By golly, this one's gotta be true, cuz it's found in ev'ry hist'ry book that's ever been printed by the Krossmyheart Press— which a' course yew know is the foremost publisher of *both of Sweden's non-fiction books.* I quote frum Chapter 17 of <u>The Pretty Much Complete And Unabridged Hist'ry Of The Swedish People</u>—

It seems that trolls wuz prevalent in Sweden before Ole's time, but not ev'ryone believed in 'em. Ole's friends didn't. Yet, there come a night when they talked Ole into joinin' 'em on a "troll hunt." Yep, yew guessed it—they wuz plannin' to trick the big guy. Their plan wuz to disappear, and leave Ole all alone out there in the graveyard, just t' see how scared he'd git.

Well, the joke wuz on Ole's friends, as the trolls wuz out in full force that night. Once ev'ry hundred years or so, it seems they'd gather frum all over Sweden just fer the heck of it, and their meetin' place wuz always the famous Troll Stone. This happens t' be a rock as big as a house—and yew'll find it down there in southern Sweden, just across the field frum the old graveyard.

Well, them trolls wuz carryin' on that night with unusual gusto, when they looked out across that field and saw Ole standin' there with his hands in his pockets. And he's not doing much of anything but tryin' to chew and whistle at the same time.

"Now, there's a chance fer some fun," snickers one troll.

"Yes, I see whut yew mean," sez anuther. "Prepare the rock!"

With that, a third troll mutters a few magic words, and the huge rock rises straight up like a elevator on eight golden pillars. Beneath it wuz the entrance to a spooky lookin' bat-filled tunnel. And it's said by some that this shaft penetrates straight on down to the core of the earth—at which place is found the domain of Satan hisself.

By this time, sev'ral trolls have gone over to the graveyard, where they round up Ole, and bring him back to the rock.

Ole meets the Trolls!

"Good golly," sez Ole. "Not never inn my yung and innocent life has I ever see'd such a rock, let alone so many trolls!"

"Heh, heh," chuckles one a' the trolls, "and not never has we see'd the likes uv yew!"

The trolls bring Ole in underneath the rock, and give him a drinkin' horn filled with a bubbly liquid.

"Now listen kareful," sez one, "cuz this is *real* important! We wants yew t' take this horn down them steps yew'll find inside the tunnel, and give it to the gent in the red suit. He'll be waitin' down there at the foot a' the stairs. Some say he ain't had a drink in years, and he'll no doubt be so glad t' have a sip that he'll grant yew whutever wish yer heart desires."

With that, Ole takes the horn with the bubbly brew. But just before he starts down them stairs, one troll warns—

"One last thing. Before yew give him that horn, make him promise to wait five minutes before drinkin' it. And yew'd best use that time t' high-tail it outa there as fast as yer legs kin go!"

Ole then descends that flight a' stairs, which winds on down like a corkscrew. No sooner is he outa sight when them trolls commence to laugh, and they roll around on the ground laughin' 'til the tears flow hot 'n heavy frum their eyes.

"He's the dumbest one yet," snorts one.

Now, the deeper Ole descends, the darker and danker things become, and he decides he's likin' this none too good. Then, far below, he makes out a faint red glow. This brightens as he descends deeper, 'til he kin make out flames, and the black silhouette of a man in front of 'em.

"Welcome to Hell," sez the devil hisself, as he sits grinnin' on a fiery throne.

"Velcome to *vere?*" sez Ole, with a gulp.

Ole & Lena

"Oh, I see. You're just another one of those dumb Swedes the trolls keep sending down here every hundred years or so," sez the devil. "I'm getting a little tired of this, and if they think I'm going to drink what's in that horn again, they must think I'm dumber than you."

"I vouldn't know nuttin' about dat," sez Ole. "Dey said dey vas yust bein' friendly—and dey struck me as bein' about as trustvorthy as any a' dem gover'mint folks up dere vere I cum frum. And fer shure dey're *more* trustvorthy den any a' yer friends down here!"

"Do you really think so?" asks the devil, who seems touched by Ole's sincerity.

Ole could tell he wuz awful thirsty, and that he *really* wanted to believe it would be differ'nt frum last time.

"Vell, Red, yer velcum two diss horn, and vutever diss bubbly stuff iss vut's in it," sez Ole, "but I rekall dem cute lil' fellers sayin' somethin' about yew granting me some kinda vish."

"Yes, yes," sez the devil, lickin' his lips in eager anticipation. "whatever you want."

"Vell," sez Ole, "Dere iss somethin'. Yew see, I hass already deweloped great prowess in higher math'matricks, and I now aspire too be a great inwentor as vell! So maybe yew kould see fit to turn me into such—dat iss, if it snot too diffikult a reqvest fer yer redship."

"No, no," sez the devil, his eyes slightly bulged and glazed. "That's not hard at all. Yes, you'll get your wish. Just give me the horn now, and do it quickly!"

"As yew vish," sez Ole. "Yew betcha fer shure! But dere iss vun ting more. Yer s'ppose too vait five minnits before yew drink it."

Ole in Hell!

"Yes, yes, of course," sez the devil. "Whatever you say. But give it to me now—quickly—so the five minutes can start immediately. Yes!"

With that, Ole hands the horn to the devil—and then he turns and scrambles back up them stairs as fast as he kin go! And all that time, he kin hear the devil countin' off them seconds and minutes until the five minutes is up.

There's a sudden flash of light down below, when the brew hits the devil's hot lips—and the muffled sound of an explosion.

"Yeepers!" sez Ole, and he covers his ears with his hands as the devil's agonized screams echo on up through the tunnel.

"THEY'VE DONE IT AGAIN, THOSE WRETCHED LITTLE CREATURES," screams the devil. "IT'S NOT THE LEAST BIT FUNNY, AND IT NEVER WAS! BUT THIS TIME THEY SHALL PAY DEARLY FOR THEIR LITTLE PRANK!"

"Uff da," sez Ole, and he clears the mouth of the tunnel runnin' like a frantic fox fleein' a hound pack, just as the Troll Stone begins to heave and shake. The ground trembles as if in the throes of a monstrous earthquake, as he scrambles out frum under the huge rock and heads fer the woods.

"No—wait, wait! Yew gotta tell us whut happened," laugh the trolls as Ole streaks on past. But their smiles turn kwickly to terror as an orange ball of flame rockets up the tunnel and explodes out frum under the rock. Blazin' trolls scatter in all directions, as the most awful sounds whut's ever been heard by folks or beasts pulsate out frum under that rock—*like a thousand or more really ticked off little tone-deaf devils screamin' off pitch all at once!*

Ole submerges hisself in a nearby lake, and watches the whole scene with only his head above water. Suddenly, there's a humongous explosion! The huge rock rises high into the night sky, and the flames beneath it take on the shape of a fiery demon.

"WHERE'S THAT SWEDE?" roars Satan's voice frum inside them flames. "SHOW YOURSELF, YOU DUMB SWEDE, WHEREVER YOU ARE!"

"Ho boy," mutters Ole to hisself. "Nobody'd be so dumb as dat!"

"ALL RIGHT THEN," bellows Satan. "YOU WANT TO BE AN INVENTOR? AN INVENTOR YOU SHALL BE! BUT *NEVER* WILL YOU *EVER* SEE ONE LOUSY PENNY FROM ANY OF YOUR INVENTIONS! YOU HEAR ME, SWEDE? NOT ONE RED CENT!"

Well, it wuz daybreak before Ole dared crawl outa that lake, to make his way back home. The Troll Stone survived intact, and yew should know that it's even been seen by yers trooly, the author hisself.[1] But ever since that fateful night of nights, trolls has ceased to be a part of Sweden's hist'ry. Well—akshully, that's not quite right. Later on, yer gonna see that one lone troll survived. In fact, that bitter critter blamed Ole fer that whole dang-blasted Troll Stone fiasco, and he swore that somehow...somewhere...someday...he would have his revenge!

Fer shure!!!

---

[1] The Troll Stone is located in Skåne, which is also known as "The Garden of Sweden." Yew'll find it just down the road from the well-known Bäckaskog Castle.

The Invention Of Lutefisk

Now, to trooly understand Ole the man, we must take time to delve into his talent fer invention. It warn't long after the Troll Stone incident that his rare inventive genius begun to bud and blossom. But oddly enough, Ole didn't consciously invent things. Most of his inventions wuz axidental. Yep, they just happened. And they happened in such a way that Ole often didn't even know he'd invented somethin'.

Ole's first great invention wuz lutefisk—and this one, like so many a' them that followed, wuz a axident. In fact, some say it's really Ole's faithful dawg and not Ole hisself who should have the credit. But I know yer itching to hear the facts and decide fer yerself, so let's commence with this epic account, taken frum Olaf Wessel's monumental sixteen volume Hist'ry of Lutefisk—

> It seems that Ole wuz out fishin' one day with his good friend Lars, and they caught themselves a heckuva mess a' cod. Well, Ole gutted all them finny critters and stacked 'em under a tree alongside his house, thinkin' he'd have hisself a tasty fried fish supper. But later on, he somehow forgot them fish, and settled fer porridge. Along about midnight, Ole's ol' Swedish Elkhound, Thor, comes onto the scene, and Thor wuz (how shall I put it?) *"stakin' out his territory."*
>
> Well, the next mornin' Ole remembers his cod pile, and when he goes lookin' fer it he finds that somethin' most remarkable has took place during the night. Namely, the cod has been transformed into a delicious new kind of edible substance.
>
> So Ole tries it again. He catches hisself some more cod, guts 'em, stacks 'em under that same tree, and leaves 'em overnight. Thor does his part,

Thor and Tree!

and the next mornin' the results is ditto, except that this time Thor hisself has et a portion.

"I'll be durned!" sez Ole. "Dis inwention bus'ness ain't half so hard as I thunk it should be."

Well, Ole repeats the whole dang thing a third time, just to be shure.

"Woof da," thinks Thor to hisself (in a Swedish accent, a' course). "Dis iss gittin' to be a verkout!" Nevertheless, the faithful dawg comes through again. The next morn, when Ole sees the results is no differ'nt, he rejoices.

"Hollylooyuh!" cries he with upstretched arms, and then he proclaims to the world that he has invented a brand new form of fish dish.

"I calls it 'Lutefisk'," sez Ole, "I named it fer my uncle, Lute Svensson, cuz—vell—too tell da troot, da smell kinda reminds me uv Lute's ol' yock strap. But dere's somethin' about it—take my verd—and furtermore, I *gwarantee* dat dawgs and Svedes frum ev'ryvhere vill find it trooly undescribubble!"

Once Lutefisk had come to be, the word spread like butter. And its appeal warn't limited to Swedes only. It seems that Skandinavians of ev'ry sort loved its slick rubbery flavor, and by year's end it wuz ofishully proclaimed to be a new basic food group.

Yet, fer some strange reason that Skandinavians won't never understand, ev'ryone else hated it like muck. Even so, Ole becum famous once folks heard he's the inventor, and he wuz pursued far and wide fer the secret. Ole said it warn't no secret at all. There's only but three ingredients—

(1) Some cod, *sez Ole*—
(2) And a tree, and—
(3) Well, he warn't too shure whut that third thing might be. All's he knowed wuz yew catch the

cod, gut 'em, stack 'em under a tree—and the
next day yew got lutefisk, by golly!

Fer shure, yew betcha!

Lars Alva Eddyson

Well, now I'm gonna shift gears fer a page or two, and
talk about Ole's good friend, Lars, who wuz fishin' with
him on that fateful day. This Lars wuz none other than
Lars Alva Eddyson, who later rose to prominence as
Sweden's *foremost* inventor—even more famous than Ole
hisself.

But alas, the story of Lars is not a pretty one. It's a
grim tale of two-faced friendship and thievin' sneakiness.
Here in this book I'm gonna tell yew the *true facts*—not
the gussied-up version that's told in most hist'ry books.
And yew'll see fer yerself that it's a sad and sorry tear-
jerker indeed—just about a two han'kerchief story.

Anyways—Lars wuz the most famous Swede inventor
in hist'ry, but the truth is that he couldn't hardly invent
somethin' hisself. The secret of his success wuz that he
possessed a unique talent that took him straight to the top
a' his profession. That wuz his talent fer stealin' ideas
frum others. And yew might as well know that Lars
preferred stealin' ideas frum other Swedes—like Ole—
cuz they wuz less apt to catch on!

Of course, most a' them Swede inventions warn't all
that good, but that didn't matter much to the Swedish
patent office. They accepted 'em all, becuz—well—*they
couldn't understand 'em anyways!*

Now then, Lars and Ole had this special relationship,
as yew'll see when we slosh on deeper into Wessel's
spellbinding <u>Hist'ry of Lutefisk</u>. This here next part tells
how Lars got filthy rich off frum lutefisk, and Ole didn't.
I quote—

Lars Alva Eddyson, workin' hardly!

Even though Ole had invented lutefisk, he never really understood the process. All's he ever had wuz a one tree production line, which didn't amount to shucks—and whutever he made he either et hisself or gave it to friends.

On the other hand, Lars Eddyson figured lutefisk wuz his red shag carpet runner to wealth and fame, so's he set out t' cash in on Ole's method fer makin' the stuff. But first he had to figure out how it worked.

Lars followed Ole about fer weeks, jottin' down each step a' the process. Finally he got t' step three, which wuz the mystery step. Lars then sat up nights, watchin' the cod pile. This warn't easy, as he always fell asleep. Yew see, Lars wuz in the habit of takin' a sleepin' pill each night at 10:00, and old habits is hard to break.

But then one night Lars run outa pills, so's he wuz finally able to stay awake. That's when he caught Ole's ol' Elkhound, Thor, makin' his essential secret contribution to the process. The mystery of the third step thus bein' solved, Lars built a huge state-of-the-art factory with thousands of trees and dawgs. And that's how "Lars, the Lutefisk King" became disgustingly rich off Ole's invention, while Ole hisself never saw one lousy cent.

But hey—this story ain't yet done. The Hist'ry of Lutefisk goes on t' tell somethin' that I myself didn't know—even though I is a great historian, well-versed in Skandinavian hist'ry. Yew see, most ev'ryone don't know this next part, cuz it's bin hushed up by the Swedish gover'mint—

The "Elkhound Lutefisk" that Lars produced in those early days wuz powerful stuff, and it sometimes had strange affects on folks who et it. Fer example, Fridtjof Nansen wuz just a pitiful sissy 'til he ate a plateful! That caused him to run off and spend three bleak long years in the Arctic, thus becomin' Skandinavia's greatest explorer.

And that famous Swede singer, Jenny Lind? Why, she suffered frum smoker's voice 'til she downed one a' them there slippery rascals—after which she had the slickest, most sweetest soprano voice that anyone's ever heard.

But there wuz a dark side, too. This cum t' light when some Elkhound Lutefisk wuz shipped on down to England, where this upstanding bishop feller named John the Pious gulped a glob. Well, it warn't long later 'til he becum knowed as Jack the Ripper—and I guess yew heard the rest a' that sad story.

Yew see—no one could ever predict whut next might happen, since *Elkhound Lutefisk affected each person differ'nt.*

Anyways, here's whatever it might be that I'm leadin' up to. It's to Lars Eddyson's credit that he did hire a team of scientists who solved the problem not long since. They replaced them Swedish Elkhounds with Mexican Chihuahuas to reduce the strength—and whut d'ya know! It turned out that "Chihuahua Lutefisk" wuz safe to eat.

However, the Swedish gover'mint wuz so ashamed of usin' Latino dawgs instead a' Swede dawgs that it did somethin' so disgustingly low that no gover'mint had ever done it before.

It concealed the facts!

And that, folks, is why yew don't never hear nuthin' about it. To this very day, *the sorry story of the Chihuahua Lutefisk remains one a' Sweden's darkest, untold national secrets!*

Okay, so there yew have it. Now yew know how Lars becum a great inventor. More important, yew also know how Ole becum a great inventor. And Ole wuz a honest-

to-gosh *real* one—not some sneaky little flop-eared fraud like Lars.

When yew think about it, it shure makes sense that someone with such a magnificent math'matical mind would also be good at inventing stuff. But then too, a' course, it didn't hurt to have some supernatural help, of which we already know fer shure that Ole had plenty of, I guess.

Whatever!

But hey—the man kept on a-churning out ideas without ever even tryin' to, sometimes on purpose and sometimes by accident. Why, he spent the whole rest of his life inventin' one darn fool thing after anuther—even though he warn't never able to cash in on none.

Once Lars Eddyson caught on to this, he'd follow Ole about day and night, stealin' his ideas—and Ole wuz never the wiser. So besides lutefisk, Eddyson snagged hisself a giant gob of other hot smash hits to boot, including—

    (1) Lars' hand carved toothpicks!
    (2) Lars' dehydrated water!!
    (3) Lars' refrigerated hot tubs!!!
             and...
    (4) Lars' high rise outhouses with walk-out basements!!!!

These wuz all Ole's inventions, to be shure, but it's Lars instead who wuz soon rollin' in kroner. So then—havin' made his fortune—the rotten little snotball had no more use fer Ole. Ruthless and callous, he bid his old fishin' friend a cold farewell, and basked in a shameful life of stolen luxury.

Ole And The King Of Sweden

Now, don't forget that this here book is about Lena too, and we'll be gittin' around to her shortly. But we're not yet done with Ole, and all his great adventures. Fer example, it's common knowledge that Ole met Lena not in Sweden but in Amerika, so yer no doubt wonderin' why he chose to leave his native land. Well, the decider wuz a case involvin' the king of Sweden, and it went somethin' like this—or so they say.[3]

It seems that Ole's fame as an inventor and a great theoretical math'matician had spread to the point where the king hisself heard tell a' him. The king then summoned Ole to the castle to be his tutor. And since Ole's specialty wuz higher math'matiks, the classes were taught in the tower of the castle.

Now, on a good day, Ole could count all the way to ten with not one mistake. Of course, one couldn't expect a king to do that, but Ole figured his highness should be able t' learn to count at least up to three—that is, if they used the old arm wrestlin' technique. By arm wrestlin' in sets of three, Ole'd be able to let the king win two times out of ev'ry three, and that way—by and by—his majesty would no doubt learn to count to three.

---

[3] This account wuz taken verbatim from a book found in the basement storage racks of the Universitetsbibliotek in Stockholm, Sweden. These racks are of excellent quality, having been made of hand-rubbed virgin spruce by Lapko (The Laplandish Kustom Furniture Kompany). Unfortunately, I don't rekall the name of the book, but rest assured that it's a good one.

So that's how it went fer the first few weeks. And I imagine things woulda continued on just fine, except that the king had a beautiful daughter named Katarina. She wuz a restless lass with a rovin' eye, and unforchoonately that eye kinda roved over towards Ole one day.

"Ole," said Princess Katarina, batting her big eyelashes in his direction. "I know that you're terribly busy with daddy all day long, and that by evening you're plumb tuckered out from all that intellectual arm wrestling stuff. So I hate to even ask. But the fact is that I sure would like to learn some numbers too, and I wondered if you'd consider squeezing me...uh, squeezing me in for lessons, that is. You know what I mean, Ole...uh, *night school?*"

"Vell, um...dat iss...(gulp)...I mean...duh," sez Ole.

After all, how kin one say "no" to a princess?

"It's settled then," sez she. "I'm usually in a math'matical mood about 8:30, and if that's true tonight, I'll stop by your room and you can teach me what happens when you have one plus one."

That evening at 8:30 sharp, Ole wuz in his room in the tower, and there come a knock on his door. Ole sprung to his feet, swung open the door, and there stood Princess Katarina lookin' very alluring indeed.

"My, aren't you the efficient one, Ole," sez she, "I see you have your blackboard all set up, and your chalk and erasers. And you also have candles and wine and a group of musicians playing soft music."

"Yes sir, uh, ma'am, dat iss, uh, I mean yer highness," sez Ole. "Ve're reddy too check out dat vun plus vun—uh, dat iss, uh—Lesson Vun...uh..."

The King and Katarina

Ole & Lena

"Oh yes, Ole, I know just what you mean. The "hands on" approach. But—my goodness—it surely is hot in here. I'm going to go and slip into something more comfortable, and then I'll be right back."

The Princess had been gone not five minutes when there wuz once again a knock at the door. Ole sprung to his feet and swung open the door, expecting the princess. But this time there stood his royal lordship, the king.

"Ole," sez he, "I'm so glad that you're still awake. I know that we wrestled with those numbers all day long, and no doubt you were looking forward to some time in bed tonight. But I've got this real urge to continue on with the lessons. I think I have that 'vun-too-tree' thing all straight now, and I sure would like to learn what comes next."

"Yes, uh...a vun, and a too, and...uh...gulp..." sez Ole, who wuz now tremblin' worse than a big fat tom turkey comin' up on Thanksgiving.

"Ole," sez the king, "you're white as torsk. Aren't you feeling well?"

Ole answered that no, he warn't feelin' too good at all, and that maybe t'morrow night might be better. But then the king wouldn't take "no" fer an answer.

"You'll feel better if you have something else to think about," he said. And then he cum right in, and set right down, and stretched his royal arm right out on the table, ready t' wrestle.

Well, Ole thunk he'd best try t' rush the lesson along by lettin' the king win a quick three times outa four. But the big guy's mind went blank. By golly, he forgot to let the king win at all. Indeed, Ole beat his highness three times outa three—*or wuz it four outa four?*

This made the king royally peeved, and he put Ole on the spot by demanding to know point blank whut comes after three.

"That should be easy as pi for a math'matician," he sez. But Ole got so nervous and flustered that he couldn't think.

"Uh...tree and a h-h-half?" he stammered.

The king wuz now beet-red with anger, and his regal teeth wuz a-gnashin', and he wuz so royally steamed that he accused the big feller of bein' a fraud.

"A tutor of higher math'matics ought at least to be able to count somewheres past three," he shouted, waving his lordly fist.

Ole argued that he coulda counted higher if the tower had been taller. And I suppose that's probably true. Anyways—it made good sense to the king, and he started calmin' down.

But just then, there's anuther knock on the door. This time it swung wide open all by itself, and there stood the king's daughter in a sheer blue nighty.

"Ole, darling," she giggled, "I'm ready to learn all about those cute little numbers of yours, just like you promised me!" But then, seein' her father sittin' there, she stopped abruptly in mid-giggle.

"Ooooops, wrong number," sez she, makin' a hasty exit.

Well, this time the king went royally berserk, and he started screamin' and throwin' a king-size tantrum!

"I DON'T NEED ANY MORE LESSONS TO SEE HOW THIS ALL ADDS UP!" he shouted, leapin' to his king-size feet and headin' down the hall after his daughter. "I'LL DEAL WITH YOU LATER, YOU FRAUD!"

Well, Ole set there for maybe two seconds, thinkin' things over. Then, realizing that his services were probubbly no longer needed, he slunk quickly down the stairs and out the back door of the castle before the king returned.

"*Uff da!*" sez Ole, who wuz now runnin' like one a' them there straight line winds. "Not only iss teachin' math hard verk, but so iss da *after-math!*"

After that, Ole figured his future wuz best spent somewheres else other than Sweden. So's he packed his bag and donned dark glasses, and headed off to the bustlin' seaport city a' Gothenburg, where all them big sturdy ocean-goin' ships wuz berthed.

Bon Voyage!

Ole on the docks at Gothenburg

Chapter Three:
Ole's Big Trek To Amerika

(or, Headin' to Minnesoty,
With Stops Along the Way)

When Ole arrived at Gothenburg, ev'ryone there wuz talkin' emigration. "Amerika fever" wuz rampant, and it wuz contagious fer shure. Men wuz lined up on the docks with wooden trunks and oilcloth bags and lotsa rowdy kids and pregnant wives—and boatloads a' folks wuz leavin' ev'ry day.

"It's da land uv oppertoonity!" sez one, grinnin' frum ear to ear with a mouthful a' chaw.

"Da streets uv Noo York City iss paved vit pure gold!" sez anuther, with the conviction that only a Swede emigrant could have.

"My unkle in Minnesoty has got hisself a pink Persian Palace on da prairie, vit hiss own private harem uv dem hefty Viskonsin bred maidens!" chimes in a third, soundin' very smug and authoritative.

"Minnesoty!" sez Ole. *"Now, dat's vun place I shure vould like too see!"*

Well, it don't take Ole long to catch the Amerika Fever, or maybe we should say the "Minnesoty Fever." He wuz all stoked up and hot to trot, but then he couldn't afford no ticket, a' course. The king had never paid him fer services rendered, and he'd never made so much as a single øre frum any a' his inventions.

Ole wuz downright desperate.

All t'gether now: *"How desperate wuz he?"*

Good golly, the big guy wuz so desperate that he stowed on board a liner, by hidin' inside a barrel a' flour!

And since Ole had his choice of ships, he chose t' stow in style. He picked none other than the big new "Amerikan Express," which wuz the sleekest, slickest, most seaworthy vessel of its kind that's ever been built. This wuz its first Atlantic crossing, but—alas—like the Titanic, the maiden voyage of this ill-fated ship would also be its last.

Now, the crossing to Amerika wuz one a' the best ever. The weather wuz mild, the ocean wuz kind, and them killer icebergs wuz nowheres to be seen. But Ole never knew it, cuz his daylight hours wuz spent hidin' in the flour. He'd climb outa his barrel only at night, and then only t' git food.

Sometimes during Ole's nightly sneak-abouts he'd be spotted—and since he wuz all white frum the flour, passengers thunk he wuz a ghost. Word spread like squirrels after nuts, and soon there wuz wide-spread bedlam on board. By the time the ship docked in Noo York City, thirty three people includin' the captain had jumped overboard and wuz presumed drowned. Anuther forty four had gone stark ravin' mad, and wuz actin' so wild that they had to be carried off in straight jackets. And all the rest wuz found under their beds, all scrunched up like yew see in them there fetus photos.

Followin' that, the "Amerikan Express" wuz quarantined fer six months in dry dock, before it wuz formally declared to be haunted.

It wuz then ofishully retired—

and never used again!

Ole's First Impressions Of Amerika

Well, the first thing Ole did in Noo York City wuz walk all over it, lookin' fer them golden streets. He never did find 'em, a' course, cuz—like one feller told him—they'd been paved over two months earlier. That same gent woulda sold Ole the Brooklyn Bridge, if he'd had any money at all fer a down payment. Plus he wuz also peddling first editions of the Bible autographed by God hisself, as many as yew want.

"Nice yung yent," thunk Ole. "A typikal Amerikan bus'nessman, no doubt. I'll shure haff too look him up vunce I git filthy rich here."

But it didn't cost nuthin' to look, a' course, so Ole continued his walk-abouts. And the more he saw, the louder he got.

"Yumpin' Yiminy!" he shouted, *"If it's only Noo York City yet, an' it's so spektakyoolar, den I kan't even begin too imagine vut Minnesoty must be like!"*

Then too, inside his brain he thunk to hisself, "A man could make his forchoon here in Amerika. Espeshully vun like me—hoo's honest as Abe, and hoo's villin' to verk hardly, and hoo's got da knack fer tinkin' up such trooly waluable inwentions!"

Ole Meets P. T. Barnum

One day—whilst Ole wuz trekkin' on down Broadway Avenue—here comes this big brick building called "The Amerikan Museum." Ole had never seen its like. It wuz jam-packed with lotsa swell displays rangin' all the way frum mummified mermaids and basketball-sized diamonds on down to Genghis Khan's false teeth and Atilla the Hun's jock strap—besides which it featured a hot humdinger of a side show to boot. And the whole dang thing wuz owned and run by one Phineas Taylor Barnum.

Ole actin' real casual
in Noo York City

Ole & Lena

As usual, P.T. hisself wuz out front hawkin' tickets that day, and by golly if he don't catch sight of Ole. Forchoonately, Barnum's own hand-writ account of this meeting has survived, and it reads as follows—[1]

Ah yes, that was the strangest sight I'd ever seen—a man who was pure white from head to toe. I thought for sure he was an albino, and I wanted him for my show. But first, I figured it wouldn't hurt to try and make a little money off him.

"Come right in, my dear pale-faced friend," said I to he most sincerely, encircling his shoulder with my arm. "Have I got a deal for you! For a mere two bits, you can browse my museum, see a live stage show, and—since you are my good friend—I'll even let you pet some of the more exotic live animals."

"Boy, it shure iss nice two know dat I's yer friend!" blurted out the big white galoot. "But I'm afeared I yust hain't got too bits!"

Well, since that was a dead-end, I went on to try and hire him. Of course everyone knows that I, the one and only Phineas T. Barnum, would one day be known and admired as the greatest showman on this whole grand planet. But at that time I was just embarking on my illustrious career, and—well—I needed something special to attract more customers. I figured that an albino just might do the trick. And so we talked for a spell. I learned that his name was Ole, and that he had achieved some small measure of fame as a great Swedish mathematician.

[1] Barnum's never-before published manuscript describing this meeting wuz found just last March in a really grungy old trunk. Sparing no expense, I outbid both Rivera Heraldoson and the Nash'nul Enquirer fer the rights to use it, and it cost me in the high two figures!

This set my mind to racing. Yes, surely I could do well with an albino Swede who could actually count to ten. But then—when I learned that Ole was the inventor of lutefisk as well—I knew I'd struck gold.

"Just imagine," said I to he. "Your name in blazing lights. Ah yes, good man, I can see it now—

OLE OSCAR SVENSSON, INVENTOR OF LUTEFISK

Why—you could be famous, my friend! And if you're willing to sweep the floors at night, you might even make a little money too!"

Now, this Ole was an "aw, shucks" kind of guy. He cared nothing for the glory of the spotlight. But he said he sure did need some cash to get to Minnesoty (of all places), and so he agreed to team up with me for a spell. And just as I thought, it was a glorious success. Ole's naive sincerity was a breath of fresh air, and his rustic charm was so magnetic that folks were drawn in from all over just to see him. My coffers overflowed, and my fame as a master showman soared higher than a Chinese sky rocket.

Well, them two hit it off real good. Before Ole cum along, nearly nobody'd paid no attenshun to Barnum, but he wuz famous after that. Of course, Ole evenshully took his annual bath, and then P.T. found out he warn't really an albino after all. But that didn't much matter. Barnum would just dust Ole with fresh flour each morning before the museum opened.

Ole, The Great Philosopher

Anyways—now that Ole wuz a celebrity, it seems that folks expected him to say profound things. And a' course, Ole didn't want to disappoint them. After all, there's lots a' precedents fer celebrities sayin' stuff to make yew think. Remember that Benjamin Franklin said—
"A stitch in time saves nine."
And some other big shot said—
"Friends...lend me yer ears."
So Ole knew right off that such sayin's don't need to make sense. They just have to be profound. So one day at the museum when he's sittin' on the stage and there's quite a crowd millin' about, Ole suddenly blurted out—
"A rolling stone plays da guitar!"
A hush fell over the room, and all eyes turned to look at the big white Swede. Slowly, folks pressed in closer and started t' murmur. Then, Ole's eyes kinda glazed over and he looked down on the crowd and said—
"Clean yer plates, kuz dere's starvin'
children in China!"
The crowd gasped. A' course, by now ev'ryone wuz so confused that they knew they must be in the presence of greatness. "Why, there's a lotta truth to that...I guess," sez a loud voice in the crowd, and then folks started to cheer. But Ole just motioned for silence, and in resonant, measured tones he uttered—
"A bird in da hand iss a real mess!"
"Write that one down quick!" somebody yelled. And next Ole sez—
"Ven da chips are down, da buffalo iss empty!"

Unforchoonately, just then Barnum showed up.
"Whoa!" sez he. "That's enough sayings for one day. Those of you who wish to hear more are welcome to come back tomorrow—*for the usual nominal admission fee, of course.*"

And after that, the crowds grew larger by the day. Ole's inventive mind just kept on churnin' out them clever sayin's, and folks remembered 'em and passed 'em on. Indeed, many a' them home-spun truths yew first heard cummin' out from b'tween yer ma's sweet lips wuz plagiarized. They first saw the light a' day whilst flowin' forth frum b'tween them two chapped lips uv Ole hisself.

Ole Discovers Tom Thumb

Big Ole really liked workin' at the museum, and he liked Barnum too. But he also liked hangin' out down the street with some new friends he'd met at Ye Olde Bowery Bar. Ole wuz doin' just that one day. Ev'ryone wuz sittin' around havin' triple-sarsaparillas and tellin' Swede jokes, like this one, fer instance—

> Question. Whut's the best thing t' come outa Sweden lately?
> Answer. *A empty boat!*

And also this one—

> Question. Whut's it say on the bottom of a Swedish pop bottle?
> Answer. *Open other end!*

Well, Ole didn't really understand them jokes, but he'd laugh anyways, cuz he knowed they wuz s'pposed to be funny. And so it went. But then, smack in the middle of anuther such joke, this customer walks in who wuz, uh— shall we say—"vertically challenged." Having never seen so short a human bein' before, Ole jumped to the wrong conclusion.

"TROLL!" he yelled. "GIT OUTA HERE KVICK!"

So said, Ole leaped fer the door, but his friends grabbed him in mid-leap.

"This here's nuthin' to be scared of," they laughed, "It's only Tom. He's a midget, and we think he's probubbly the smallest in the world."

Small he wuz, by golly, even fer a midget. In fact, that little rascal wuz as short as Ole wuz tall!

"How's the weather up there, big guy?" squeaked the midget, and Ole thunk it wuz so funny that he laughed 'til tears cum squirtin' outa his eyeballs.

"By yumpin' Yiminy, I gotta take yew too meet my good friend, Barnum!" he whooped, whilst wipin' his cheeks with his sleeve. "He kullects all kinds a' veird stuff, but he hain't got nuttin' too kompare two da likes uv yew! Yew play yer cards right, Tom, and I bet he'll vant too kullect yew too!"

But now let's scoot back to Barnum's moldy old manuscript, and let the great showman hisself tell whut happened next—

> I must admit that for a dumb Swede, Ole was pretty smart when it came to new ideas. I never knew what he'd come up with next. But this time the lad really outdid himself. I was sitting in my office one day, when in he comes with this miniature man who was no larger than a number 2 Kewpie doll.
>
> "Barnum, ol' buddy, I vants yew too meet my new friend Tom," says he to me. "Dis here fella's as small as a Svedish troll, except dat—vell—by gum, he's even smaller! *Yenerally* speakin', I'd say dat *Tom* ain't no bigger'n my *tumb!*"
>
> Ole's words set me to thinking. "General... *Thumb.* Yes, that's it. I'll call him—
> GENERAL TOM THUMB!
> The public will flock to see a midget who's as small as this one, with a catchy name to boot."

So Barnum hired the short guy, and frum then on he wuz the star attrackshun at Barnum's show. The master showman becum the toast of the town, and Thumb wuz the hottest hit he ever had.

But hey—yew kin see fer yerself it wuz all thanks to Ole!

P.T. Barnum
and Tom Thumb

"Dat Tom—by golly if he ain't da cutest lil' *sucker* vut's ever bin *born,* and I *mean it!"* sez Ole.

Barnum overheard this, and coined the phrase—

"THERE'S A SUCKER BORN EVERY MINUTE."

Yew've heard that one, a' course. It ain't too nice, but I guess there's a lotta truth to it anyways. Fer shure it's the kind a' thinkin' that made Barnum rich. But I'll bet yew ten-two-one that yew never knew this phrase wuz inspired by Ole hisself, whose inventive powers wuz constantly runnin' amuck in his vokabulary.

The sad part is, it wuz someone else other than Ole who got rich—as usual!

Lars Eddyson Comes To Amerika

Meanwhile, that slimy little barfbag, Lars Eddyson, had already squandered his vast fortune on wild livin' and (heh, heh) even wilder Swedish women, so's he headed fer Amerika, hopin' to find Ole and steal some more a' his ideas. Bein' broke, the sad little scumball made the trip by stowin' inside the flour barrel on the ill-fated "Amerikan Express II."

Shure enough, that unforchoonate vessel ends up quarantined right alongside the Amerikan Express I *(and fer the exact same reason, I might add).* However, Lars manages to slip offa the boat, after which he spots Ole's name and picture on a giant billboard. That leads him straight to Barnum's on Broadway, and a big hand-slappin' whoop-de-doo reunion with his old fishin' pal.

Now, Ole wuz real glad to see Lars, but Barnum warn't. Fer one thing, two albinos wuz one too many. And fer anuther thing, P.T. saw through that little flour-covered shyster right off, y' see, cuz they both had somethin' in common. *That is, they wuz both tryin' to git rich off a' Ole's ideas!*

Well, by the time this sorry story wuz done, they'd both managed to cash in on a few—and by golly there wuz plenty t' go around, cuz Ole shed ideas like a bear sheds its winter fur come spring!

But then, Lars got real greedy and decided he had t' git Ole away frum Barnum. Lars wanted *all* them ideas hisself, you see. So's he talked Ole into leavin' Noo York City, in search of greener pastures.

"Dere's fortunes to be made out yonder," sez Lars, wavin' his hand in a westerly direction.

That set just fine with Ole, a' course, since he still wanted t' git to Minnesoty. But first, he did Barnum one last favor by puttin' him on to Jenny Lind, the sweet-singin' Swede with the warbling voice.

"She kouldn't hold a note 'til she gulped down summa my lutefisk," said Ole. "Vell, dat flushed her pipes—and now da little lady sings yust like a *night'ngull,* and packs 'em in frum vun end a' *Sveden* too da udder!"

So Barnum brought Lind to Amerika and promoted her as "THE SWEDISH NIGHTINGALE," which wuz also a dad-gum monstrous huge success.

Ole and P.T. parted company after that, though P.T. insisted—shrewdly—that they keep in touch. Ole sent Barnum lots more ideas over the years, and the old showman becum rich as cheesecake becuzza them.[2]

The Wizard of Menlo Park

Well, Lars and Ole left Noo York City headin' west, but they didn't git too far. Ole wuz navigatin', yew see, and they warn't no further along than Noo Jersee when they got lost.

---

[2] Later on, Barnum published a autobiography of his life 'n times, and to this day there's copies at yer lokul library. But don't look fer Ole in that book. Barnum never did mention him, cuz he wanted all the credit hisself, a' course.

Anyways, they wound up in some small town called Menlo Park, where perchance a young Amerikan inventor had just set up shop. But the poor chap wuz strugglin' somethin' awful, cuz he wuz findin' out that inventions ain't all that easy to invent!

Young Thomas Edison wuz fresh out of ideas, it seems, and he just didn't know whut t' do next!

Well, Tom took a likin' to them two poor lost Swedes—Ole in partikyoolar—so's he talked 'em into stayin' a while.

"You'll feel right at home here," sez Tom. "Most folks say Noo Jersee's just like Sweden—except that Sweden's quiet and peaceful, and it's got clean air and unpolluted lakes, and nice people."

"Vell—Noo Jersee shure duz sound like my kinda place!" sez Ole. "But, den a' course ev'ryplace iss, to tell da trooth."

So then one night them boys wuz just sittin' around gabbin' and spittin', when young Edison gets all teary-eyed and serious. And suddenly he blurts out that things just warn't goin' too good fer him of late.

"Like fer example, just last week I invented the phonograph," he blubbered. "But it just sits there and don't do nuthin' at all that I kin see!"

Then Tom buried his face in his hands, sobbin' somethin' awful, and sez he's about ready t' give up on it.

"Vell, Tom," sez Ole, puttin' one hand on the young man's shoulder, "I shure vould like to help! Maybe if yew vould yust let me review yer records..."

"Whoa!" shouts Tom, leapin' suddenly to his feet. *"Records!* Glory be if that ain't the answer!"

And once Tom had invented records, his phonograph turned out to be one big slam-bang mega-colossus high-five success. He wuz famous after that, a' course, and folks started callin' him "the Wizard of Menlo Park!" *But I guess the truth is that it's really Ole who wuz the wizard.*

Time Fer A Pause

Well—yew folks have been real attentive readers up 'til now, and I shure do appreciate that. So right here then I'm callin' a short recess, to give yew time to go t' the bathroom, or do whutever else it is yew have t' do. And then when yer done, we'll pick up right where we left off.

(Break time. Allow up to ten minutes.)

Yer back again so soon? Yew didn't wash yer hands then, did yew? My mother always said yew should wash yer hands. Okay? But yew better hurry. Yew only got five more minutes.

(I wuz gonna use this time to go out fer a smoke, but then I remembered I don't smoke.)

So yer all washed and dried? All right then. Back to the story.

The Invention Of The Light Bulb

Anyways—Ole's ma wuz a real fine cook, by golly, and back when he wuz packin' t' go to Amerika she'd sent along a Mason jar filled with her specialty—
HELGA SVENSSON'S HOME-CANNED LUTEFISK.
In time, Ole'd et 'most all there wuz—except fer one last hunk. And he kept that so's whenever he wuz in the mood fer his favorite treat, he could unscrew the lid and enjoy the smell. As time went by and fermentation set in, the jar begun t' glow at night—and the older it got the brighter it glowed.

"Vut yew got in dat dere yar?" Lars Eddyson asked one day.

Ole told him whut, which set Lars t' thinkin'. And by and by, it clicks that "light jars" would be a swell replacement fer kerosene lamps. The greedy little greaseball then made plans to produce such jars, bein' dead shure that once again he'd struck the mother lode!

"By Yiminy," sez Lars to hisself, "vunce *Lars' Light Yars* goes nationvide, dem bucks vill kum rollin' in faster den basketballs bouncin' down a ski slope!"

After that, the little wart-faced leech wuz so caught up with bus'ness plans that he had no more time fer Ole, so's he sent him packin'.

"Yew trek on vesterly ahead," he said coldly. "I'll ketch up too yew later!"

Ole then left Noo Jersee, and set off alone in the gen'ral direction of Minnesoty, though he wuz in no big hurry t' git there (it seems that few folks is, even to this very day). And once again, it looked as if that zit-faced ugly little pip-squeak Lars would git rich and Ole wouldn't.

But there is a higher justice, folks, and as the author of this book, I decided it wuz high time that Lars got whut wuz comin' to him. So here's how he got a taste of his own medicine—

It seems that Eddyson's factory wuz located right next door t' Edison's factory, and—well—there wuz a secret tunnel betwixt 'em. I guess most historians is too dumb to know that Tom "acquired" most of his ideas by usin' that very tunnel at night to check up on Lars' ideas. *And danged if they warn't the exact same ideas that Lars had burgled frum Ole!*

Light jars is a prime example. Before Lars had cashed in his chips on that one, Tom Edison jumped in and trumped his hand. It seems that Tom wuz foolin' around with a Eddyson jar one night (which he had acquired whilst usin' that tunnel), and he put a hot electric wire inside it to burn off the smell. The result wuz the "Lutefisk Gas Light Bulb," which Tom shrewdly called the "Vacuum Light Bulb" to confound the competition. Once this bulb hit the market, light jars wuz out, and the rest wuz hist'ry.[3]

After that, Eddyson fell on tough times. Ole wuz gone, and without his help Lars tried desperate hard to invent his own stuff, none of which ever quite caught on. Some that *almost made it* included—

    (1) Lars' Singlemint gum.
    (2) Lars' 5-shooter revolvers,
        and...
    (3) Lars' 6-Up soda pop.

And some that wuz *total duds* included—

    (4) Lars' lutefisk fruitcake.
    (5) Lars' unscented perfume.
    (6) Lars' biodegradable swimsuits,
        and...
    (7) Lars' 4th of July ice fishing contests.

3 Most folks don't know that light bulbs is filled with lutefisk gas to this very day.

Ole & Lena

A rare picture uv Tom Edison & Lars Eddyson hangin' out t'gether

Well, Lars lost ev'rything he had promoting that awful string of no-good losers, and then he disappeared. Most folks thunk he'd gone back t' Sweden. But the truth is that he wuz too ashamed fer that, so's he'd slunk off to hide in Norway. All in all, it wuz a tad sad—and a sorry end fer Sweden's most famous inventor, *even if he wuz a thievin' double-ugly snoose bucket!*

The Invention Of The Aeroplane

Meanwhile, Ole wuz trekkin' on west. He warn't never gonna see Lars again, but he didn't know that yet, a' course. Anyways—he soon arrived at Daytun, O'hio, where he chose t' rest a spell. And darned if he didn't meet a couple a' tricycle repairmen who wuz also amateur inventors. They wuz the famous Wrong Brothers, and their names wuz Torville and Dilbert.

Well, Ole hit it off real good with them boys, he too bein' an inventor and such. Ole soon learned they wuz into aeronautics. Moreover, they believed they wuz real close to havin' a machine that could akshully fly—a "aeroplane," they called it. Ole wuz stayin' at Aimee Bordello's Boarding House at the time, the one down on Willow Street with the big red light in the second story window.

Of course yew've heard of Aimee's diary, I s'ppose. The one that caused the big scandal when it wuz published a few years later, under the provocative title of "Aimee's Uncensored X-Rated Memoirs." Well, there's informashun in that diary that's vital to the next part of our story. And that hit me hard with a awful dilemma, cuz whut I needed wuz mixed in with a whole slew a' juicy tidbits that can't be quoted in a family book like this.

Well, I used it anyways, by golly—but only after extensive editing fer language and content, and to fit the space available. So anyways, here's whut's left of Aimee's own words—

Ooooh—goodness, yes, I remember it well! Ole and them Wrong boys wuz sittin' right here in my parlor, talkin' real loud and partakin' of my special Jasmine tea and my even more specialer lutefisk petits fours. Yes!—they wuz so masculine, them three. And as usual they wuz diskussin' such manly things. Technikal stuff, y' know—things which wuz way over *my* poor little head!

"Ole, tell me whut yew *really* think!" sez that dreamy Dilbert. "Is it trooly probable that a man could fly like the birds?"

"Yah, shure, yew betcha," drawled Ole with that suave, sophisticated Swedish accent a' his, as I run my fingers through his glorious carrot-colored hair. "But flyin's da easy part," sez he. "It's da dad-gum landings vut vorries me!"

Ooooh—thinkin' about that big, rugged Swede still makes me smile! The gorgeous galoot wuz completely harmless—and as innocent as a newborn lamb. But he blushed so easy that I couldn't help but tease him. And whenever I did, his face would turn beet red and clash somethin' awful with his hair. As I recall, there wuz any number of ways I could make him blush. Fer example...

Whoa! Censored!!! There's a whole bunch got deleted here, and with good reason. In fact, I had t' skip way down to the part where Aimee starts talkin' about them Wrong Brothers—

So then I'm gonna tell yew about Torville and Dilbert. Mercy sakes now, them boys wuz anything *but* innocent! And they wuz *yes!*—oh so handsome with their curly mustaches and all—and they had such firm muscles that it gived me the shivers! Them boys wuz, ooooh, always fiddlin' around—uh—in the back of their tricycle shop, that is. Moreover, they wuz...

Ho boy! Censored again! One more whole page gits the axe! Uh—make that a page and a half. Let's drop on down to the part where Aimee tells about the aeroplane—

Well, rumors had it that them brothers wuz makin' a Frankenstein monster. No one knew fer shure, a' course—not even poor, helpless little ol' me. That Ole, he wuz really the only one they confided in.

Then, one fine June day we all found out whut'd bin so secret. Torville and that dreamy Dilbert wheeled out a genuine honest-to-gosh aero-thingy—no doubt the first whut'd ever bin. Ooooh—whut a slick, sleek, fine-tuned machine that wuz! They planned to taxi it on down Willow Street straight past my house, pickin' up speed 'til it reached a red wooden ramp—at which time it would woosh straight up into the sky!

Ooooh—I shan't *never* forget how splendid that big ol' *(censored)* aero-thingy looked. It wuz made a' the finest, hand-whittled willow sticks, and it looked kinda just like a big oversized tricycle with frilly Tinkerbelle wings and a tail like a big lacy valentine heart. And my goodness! Wouldn't yew know that all its essential parts wuz covered with shiny red silk—which it turns out wuz made frum sum a' my old Munsingwear dresses.

Them two brothers—they both looked, *yes!*— ooooh, oh so macho in their shiny black patent leather boots, and their patent leather helmets, and their patent leather bomber jackets labeled "Confederate Air Force." They wuz so dashing that—mercy me—I coulda swooned. And they had matching red silk shirts under those patent leather jackets, which wuz made not frum my dresses, but frum some a' my other garments, such as my red Munsingwear...

Whoops! That one almost slipped through.

Them boys wuz ready t' launch, I do recall. But then at the last minute, Ole pipes up and sez he thunk their engine wuz not powerful enough.

"Soopercharge it vit lutefisk fumes," wuz his suggestion.

This provoked a heated discussion between Dilbert and Torville. Them two both huddled under the remains of a big old willow tree in my front yard and argued back and forth. And once, I thunk Dilbert wuz gonna smite Torville with his patent leather glove. Ooooh—thank goodness it never come to that—though it did cause my frail heart to go "pitty-pat," and it also caused me to...

Uff da! That wuz just awful!

And then I felt so faint that Ole had t' hold me frum falling.

And finally, they agreed to try a *half portion* of lutefisk fumes, which they said brought the octane level up to about 263.

And suddenly it wuz launch time!

"Contact," yelled Dilbert, spinning the prop as his brother sat on the large patent leather tricycle seat. Teeth bared, Torville tightened the strap on his patent leather helmet, and pulled down them silver-lensed goggles over his bulging, dilated eyes. I gived him a big, wet kiss fer luck, and—*mercy sakes!*—wouldn't yew know his breathin' sounded jus' like one a' them obscene phone calls that I'd git on Tuesdays and Thursdays, and...and...*Ooooh!*

Torville's big sweaty hands clutched them handle grips as the powerful engine came to life, and that big red silky aero-thingy set there twitchin' and belchin' like a wild animal in heat.

"On tree," cried Ole. "Vun!...Too!..."

"*Geronimo-o-o-o-o!*" yelled Torville, and then their voices wuz drowned out by the scream of the engine. The great machine lurched forward like a big crazed male lion chasin' his mate! On down Willow Street toward the red ramp it roared, bouncing up and down along on the cobblestones and pickin' up speed as it headed straight fer its destiny!

But then—suddenly—that big ol' lacy thingy commenced to shake like a drenched ol' hound dawg dryin' hisself! Its engine wuz a-screamin' like a ravin' lunatic, louder and shriller 'til I had to brush back my fresh-washed red curls, and cover my dainty little ears with my even more daintier little red-nailed hands. Louder it roared, and louder still!—soundin' sorta like giant-sized corn a-poppin'. And then—*mercy me!*—thick clouds a' white steam puffed out frum the exhaust, blockin' our view as the thingy hit the ramp!

"(Bleep)!" I shrieked.

"Great yumpin' Yiminy!" gasped Ole.

I stretched high on my tippy toes to see, arching my graceful neck as best I wuz physically able. And suddenly, there come a big boomin' explosion that knocked me right on my...

Censored!!!

"Uff da!" yelled Ole—and then I see'd him stagger backwards, hands clapped tight to his ears, as a big red silky-looking ball a' fire and a mushroom-shaped plume a' thick red smoke rose high over the spot where the ramp used to be!

There followed a solemn moment of silence, as Ole and Dilbert just stood there kinda dumbfounded. Then with heads bowed low, they took off their hats and held 'em to their manly chests, as scraps of shredded silk come floatin' down all over—kinda like big red Munsingwear snow flakes.

Did that unfortunate aero-thingy akshully fly before the dreadful explosion occurred? Well, I

The Wrong Brothers' Aeroplane
(Top secret classified photo)

Ole & Lena

myself sorta thunk so, I guess, and so did lots of others. But Ole and Dilbert had a differ'nt view, and they said no. I guess no one knows fer shure. "I doubt she *ever* voulda flu," muttered Ole, shakin' his head. "Dat patch on da ving yust vouldn't a' held. Now, if yew'd a' patched it vit da flap frum Uncle Hjalmer's red long yohns insteada dat dere lacy silky stuff, it voulda stood a chance!"

So there yew have it. Aimee Bordello's own somewhut censored words, taken straight frum her gilt-edged, sweet-smellin' memoirs. But there's a footnote to add, cuz somethin' else of great importance happened on that fateful day—somethin' that Aimee herself didn't know. Yew see, there wuz *anuther* pair a' brothers standin' right alongside Ole when he uttered them historic words about his Uncle Hjalmer.

"Did you hear that, Wilbur?" asked his brother Orville. "Flaps! That should do the trick. Flaps on the wings! Yes, that has to be the answer we've been looking for—the *wright* answer!"

The Great Chikago Fire

Followin' that awful fiasco with the Wrong brothers, Ole decided it wuz trekkin' time again. He wuz tired of O'hio anyways, so's he packed his belongin's into his brand new red silk duffel bag (which wuz a hand-stitched "ferget-me-not" present frum Aimee herself), and aimed hisself straight towards that big new wooden waterfront town in the Amerikan heartland—the one they call Chikago. He planned to tarry there a while or two, before headin' on up t' Minnesoty.

Arrivin' at Chikago, Ole stopped in at a tinder-dry clapboard house with a tinder-dry wooden "room fer rent" sign out front. And hey—there's a second tinder-dry sign just above it that read "Mrs. O'Leary's Boarding House."

Yew guessed it, a' course! This wuz *the* infamous Mrs. O'Leary—the one whose name is burned into Chikago's hist'ry books as the owner of a equally infamous (alleged) arsonist cow.

So who *really* burned down the town? The despicable cow, yew say. Yew saw that in some hist'ry book, didn't yew?

Well, *them hist'ry books is dead wrong again, as usual!*

Fer shure it wuz *not* Mrs. O'Leary's cow who burned down Chikago. And once again, *this* book is gonna give yew the *true* facts. Read on, dear reader, and yew shall be inducted into the exalted inner circle of them enlightened few who knows whut *really* happened on that fateful flamin' Oktober night.

The following obscure historical dokument has cum into my hands just lately. It claims to be the sworn testimony of Mr. Patrick O'Leary hisself, given on his deathbed after downing twelve shots of whiskey.[4] I quote as follows—

> Listen careful now if it's truth yew seek! Sure, I admit t' bein' Mrs. O'Leary's husband, and I can't (hic) deny that she owned a cow. Patrick(hic)'s my name, if yew care t' know.
>
> Now there's rampant rumors galore, and I guess they can't all be wrong. Yes, it's true then—like they say—that I had a wee bit uv a taste fer the white lightning. But here on my deathbed, I swear that it warn't exact(hic)ly my fault that things got so outa hand. Our problems all started the day the big Swede showed up on our doorstep.
>
> Not that things wuz his fault neither, mind yew. He wuz likable enuf, and his intentions wuz sterling, but it seems that trouble followed him around like gnats after road-kill.

4 Which is probably why he wuz on his deathbed.

O'Leary Family Portrait
(In happier times).

The Missus wuz lookin' fer someone t' work in the cow barn, and Ole—he wuz awful fond uv flapjacks fer breakfast. So they made a deal then, him and her—a free room and all the flapjacks he could eat, in exchange fer tending the barn. This turned out t' be a far better deal fer Ole than fer the Missus, cuz Ole could put away one (hic) heckuva lot a' flapjacks! Anyways—that's how the big Swede becum our hired hand in the first place.

Now, this Ole—he wuz kinduva (hic) amateur inventor. One night then, while he's tending the barn and wishin' he warn't, the idea popped right into his skull fer a neat little contraption that he called "The Ole-automatik Cow Barn Lantern Timer." It would light the old kerosene lantern each night at dusk, and snuff it at ten. This nifty gizmo looked a wee bit like a rat trap, except it wuz powered by this big brass clock(hic) spring that needed winding only once a week. This took care uv Ole's after-supper chores, so's he needn't hang out all night in the barn. And since Ole and me wuz now good buddies, it gived us leeway to slip out t' do the town t'gether—and me Missus wuz never the wiser.

One night then, when Ole'd had one drink (hic) too many (which fer Ole wuz one drink), he told me a soopernatural tale about trolls and a Troll Stone, and a staircase to hell. If yew'da heard me laugh, yew'da knowed right off that I thunk it wuz blarney. But I wuz about t' learn I wuz wrong. Cuz it seems that the last remaining troll had followed Ole to Amer(hic)a, vowin' revenge fer that calamitous big blast-out back there in Sweden. That sinister little runt had made the trip by stowin' away in the flour barrel on the ill-fated "Amerikan Express III."

Ole & Lena

Ah yes, may that unforchoonate haunted vessel forever rust in peace (hic).

Now, how this troll homed in on Ole and found him, I'll never know. Troll magic, I guess. But then he took up residence in the rafters uv our cow barn, and there he set, frettin' and stewin' and thinkin' up ways t' bring down grief on the big Swede. Late one afternoon, me Missus happened t' spot the little flour-coated varmint sittin' up there pondering, and the next day at break(hic)fast she sez,

"Guess whut, Patrick. We have a wee white leprechaun out in the barn. Surely that means good luck, don't yew think?"

"Sounds more like a stow-away troll to me," sez Ole between pancakes, "and fer dad-gum shure dat means *bad* luck."

And as fer me—I kept my mouth shut. But I had this *really sick feeling* about the whole thing!

Well—that night, me and Ole wuz returnin' frum a big night on the town. We wuz feelin' quite musikal, cuz Ole'd had his one drink, and I'd had a few (hic) myself, and we wuz yodeling the 12th stanza uv the Swedish Nash'nul Anthem. Then, suddenly, there he wuz—the wee one! And he wuz the dad blamed *strangest* little critter I ever laid eyes on!

"TROLL!" yells Ole,
        "GIT OUTA HERE KVICK!"

The nasty little black-eyed runt looked up, startled, cuz we'd caught him booby-trappin' the timer. He'd just finished fixin' it, such that Ole woulda been done in by a humongous pitchfork the next time he wound it up. The wee rascal wuz crouched down by the cow at the time, holdin' the ker(hic)osene lantern.

At that fateful moment when Ole yells "Troll," the cow gits so scared that she lets out a bellow. This makes the troll jump. He bumps the timer, which goes "Ker-chunk" (hic), and then the big seven day spring unwinds all at once, with a noise that sounds kinda like—

"fooooooooooooiiiiiiiiiiiiing."

This launches first the troll and then the pitchfork into the air.

"Yee-haw-hoo-hoo-hoooooooo!"

yells the troll, as with lantern in hand he sails clear across the barn and into the straw pile—with the pitchfork sailin' right behind.

The lantern glass breaks, and suddenly flames is ev'rywhere. Mrs. O'Leary wuz just comin' up outside the barn, when the frantic little bug-eyed boob bursts through the door, all bound up in springs like a bronze mummy and yellin'—

"Yee-(hic)-haw-hoo-hoo-(hic)hoooooooo!"

He's runnin' like yer nose, trailin' smoke and flames, with a red hot pitchfork stickin' out frum the seat uv his pants. The troll dives headlong into the manure pile, causin' a

"pbfffzzzbbwwzzzbbhssst"

kind a' sound. Then, all the Missus sees is thick black smoke comin' outa the (hic) hole in the pile, along with a smell she sez is best fergot.

The Missus pokes her head through the blazin' door of the blazin' barn, and there's the poor innocent cow, jumpin' up and down all wild-eyed and bellowin'. But since it's still all tied up, the Missus knows right off that the cow didn't do it. By then, it wuz too late t' stop the fire. Chikago's known as the "windy city," y' know, and—well—I guess we *all* know whut happened after that!

SCENIC CHIKAGO

"Wish yew wuz hear!"

Anyways—once the flames wuz out and Chikago wuz toast, the usual buck-passin' commenced. Folks wuz trackin' the fire's path, and closin' in on our cow barn—or whut wuz left uv it, that is. Ole and us O'(hic)Leary's, we tried t' figure out whut we should say if they tried t' blame it on us. We knowed the troll done it, a' course, but he warn't nowheres t' be found—and we didn't even know if he's alive or dead.

"Ole," sez the Missus, "if we tell the truth and blame it on the wee leprec(hic)haun, they'll think it's blarney. There's just too many skeptics around fer that."

"We gotta think a' somethin' right quick(hic) then," I added, "or fer shure they'll blame it all on us!"

Then, alluva sudden Ole's face lights up brighter than the great inferno itself. *"Yee viss by Yiminy, I got it!"* sez he. *"Ve'll blame it on da kow!"*

And so we did.

And that wuz that.

Pure and simple.

Yep (hic).

That then is the deathbed testimony of Patrick O'Leary hisself, signed with a big X on the bottom, and solemnly witnessed by one mostly sober notary public, and three hardly sober bystanders. Now, either this dokument is as false as yer teeth, or them hist'ry books is wrong. Fer shure I know which one I believe, becuz—duh—who's gonna tell lies on their deathbed?

But in the long run, I guess that yew, the reader, will just have t' choose which version of that flamin' fiasco works best fer yew.

At Last, Ole Arrives In Minnesoty

Anyways—since there warn't much left a' Chikago, and fer shure it wuz slim pickin's fer cow tenders, Ole decided to move on again. The O'Leary's held a swell outdoor farewell party fer him *(there warn't no indoors no more)*, topped off with a big beef bar-B-que *(which wuz very practical, since the meat wuz already cooked).*

Now then, Ole wuz real glad to be so close t' Minnesoty, and eagerer than ever to git there. So it wuz with Joy that he left Chikago then, and headed north, traversin' miles of furrowed fertile farmland. Finally, he see'd a big sign loomin' up ahead, and when he read whut it said, he jumped fer Joy.

Well, Joy slapped his face and left!

But Ole didn't mind much. He wuz all excited, cuz that sign sez—

MINNESOTY, LAND OF 10,000 LAKES
(COUNT 'EM YERSELF)

"Hollylooyuh!" whooped he then. And as he kontinued north alone, he begun to count them lakes while he went. Unforchoonately, things got all confused once he passed ten, but that did not damp his spirits. Before yew know it, he'd followed that lake chain right on up t' northern Minnesoty, where lumberjackin' wuz hot, and the great north woods wuz alive with the hard-workin' sounds and smells of choppin' and sawin'.

Ole Meets Paul Bunyan

After a couple a' flings at smaller loggin' camps, where things went sorta okay at best, Ole's luck took a rare flip fer the better. He had the good fortune to meet up with that greatest of all legendary loggers—Paul Bunyan hisself! Well, him and Paul sized each other up—and by golly if they warn't both highly impressed!

Minnesoty, Finally!

Even though Paul wuz just a young guy who warn't yet volumetrically maximized, he wuz still a substantial man—bigger than Ole by a good stretch, and by far the largest that Ole'd ever met.

Ole commenced t' sign up with Ol' Paul fer a hitch, after which they spent some seasons lumberjackin' t'gether in north woods Minnesoty. Paul wuz just startin' out back then, and him and Ole wuz good buddies through all the legendary years.

Paul needed a blacksmith, and even though Ole wuz ignorant of the fine art of hot metal-workin', Paul taught him ev'rything he ever knew, and more besides. Paul called Ole "the Big Swede." And those of yew who's read them popular Paul Bunyan saga tales will remember that, cuz that's whut Paul's blacksmith wuz always called—

Ole, the Big Swede!

Of course, there's no need to repeat those stories here. Such classics as "The Whistling River" and "The Giant Bullsnake" kin be found in them Paul Bunyan adventure books. But there's one true tale that, so far as I know, has escaped the notice of Paul Bunyan historians ev'rywhere, and's not never before appeared in print—until now, that is. It's the story of the great Big Woods Annual Arm-Wrestling Championship. Perchance, that wuz also the night when Ole's arch-enemy the troll showed up at the loggin' camp, still alive and seekin' revenge fer them awful "incidents" back there in old Sweden and down yonder in whut's left a' Chikago. An old logger thunk back to whut happened that dreadful night, and writ it down as follows—

Yesiree folks! Fer shure the Big Woods Arm-Wrestlin' bash wuz somethin' not to be missed, cuz it's times like this when legends is born! And so the camp wuz packed full to burstin', then, as 'jacks and drifters drifted in frum far and wide with their whole families in tow. A great canvas tent wuz sewed special fer the fete, capable of' holdin' 220,000 souls. Even so, it couldn't come close t' containin' us all that night, hardly, and there's plenty who'll tell yew they never got in.

There wuz food booths and fortune tellers and carnival rides.

There wuz log rollin' and tree climbin' and tobaccy spittin' contests.

And Babe, the Mighty Blue Ox wuz on hand, givin' bare-back rides to 137 folks at once.

The arm-wrestlin' championship of the world wuz set fer midnight, with warm-ups first, and this year featurin' Paul versus Ole in the main event. The odds wuz running 60-40 in favor a' Paul, and them two wuz both busy showin' off by flexin' their biceps and takin' on challengers frum amongst us on-lookers and by-standers. By 10 PM, I'd judge that 40 per cent a' the men had their arms in slings—*and so did 10 per cent a' the women!*

So it wuz just about then when this strange lookin' little runt shows up. He wuz kinda burnt and crispy-lookin', with a row of little round holes in the seat of his pants. *And darned if he warn't as ugly as the face in yer mirror! (heh, heh).*

Well—anyways—he walks up to Paul, extends an arm and sez, "Put 'er there, big guy. That is, if yer ready to wrestle."

Now, I didn't yet know that the runt wuz a troll, or I'd a' been terrified. But since yew know better (seein' as I just told yew), the first thing yer no doubt askin' yerself is,

"Whut on earth is a troll doin' in Paul Bunyan's loggin' camp?"

And the second thing is,

"Why has he challenged the likes a' Paul to a arm-wrestlin' match?"

Well, right up front here I'll tell yew that no one

knows fer shure! Later on—in the weeks that followed, we all pooled our heads and tried to reckon it out—and I think we finally got it figured, mostly. No doubt, the black-eyed runt wuz out to git Ole, and he musta thunk he'd have t' git rid a' Paul first—before he'd have a shot at the big Swede.

Anyways, Paul looks down at the runt. Seein's he never heard a' trolls before and had no idea whut they're capable of, he laughed so hard the ground shook.

"By jingo, yer a wee one," chuckled Ol' Paul. "Fer yew, I'll jus' use my little finger."

"Heh, heh," sez the troll, rollin' up his sleeve. "Yer choice."

Now, all those who wuz sober and wuz standin' near the runt agrees he wuz up to no good. There's one who swears the little fella had a fistful a' thumb tacks and razor blades. That's doubtful. Anuther claims he see'd him readin' a book called Troll's Handbook of Nasty Magic Tricks. That's possible. But to my judgement, the most likely case cums frum old Sven "Peg Leg" Peterson, a veteran logger who once sawed off his own leg with a hand saw—by accident, a' course.

It seems that Sven once see'd a troll in a arm-wrestlin' match back in old Sweden. And Sven sez that right at the last minute, just after all the bets wuz placed, that troll muttered a magic word soundin' somethin' like—

"Rutabagasn'rommegraut."

Why—suddenly the troll's arm swells up so big that it's a giant 16 footer with a little guy attached to it! The arm then takes on a life of its own, and proceeds to wipe out ev'ryone in sight, first beatin' 'em in arm wrestling, and then pounding 'em flat like a big hammer.

Now, if yer a bettin' person, I'll bet yew one week's wages that the troll at Paul's camp wuz gonna use the "big arm" trick too. And if yew take that bet, then yer dumber than I thunk.

Well, once the crowd hears that Paul and the runt is gonna square off, they go nuts. The odds rise quickly to 1000 to 1, favorin' Paul. Even Ole cums over to see whut the ruckus is all about. But when he does, the troll's cover is blown.

"TROLL!" yells Ole,
        "GIT OUTA HERE KVICK!"

The troll knows right off that he's lost the element of surprise, which a' course to trolls is highly important. Now, bein' flat-out flustered, the little rascal gits all tongue-tied and sez—
        "tuargemmor'nsagabatuR"
instead a'—
        "Rutabagasn'rommegraut."
And in case yew don't know and yer too dumb t' figure it out, "tuargemmor'nsagabatuR" is "Rutabagasn'rommegraut" spelled backwards!

Suddenly, the troll's arm—insteada swelling up to be 16 foot long—shrinks down to be only 1.6 inches long.

"Uh oh," sez the troll kinda sheepish-like, and heads fer cover.

Anyways—at the exact moment when Ole sez "Troll," unbridled chaos breaks loose ev'rywhere! All the Skandinavians both inside and outside the tent panic, and throngs of men, women, dawgs, and kids jam the doorways. Those inside the tent is pushin' and shovin' and strugglin' t' git out, whilst those outside is pushin' and shovin' and strugglin' t' git in.

Wild chaotic pandemonium reigns!

Rampant riots is ragin' ev'rywheres!

Ole's good buddies
Paul and Babe

Ole & Lena

Chairs is throwed, and dawgs is throwed, and even folks is throwed! And Ol' Paul is tryin' all the while to calm things down—but that just don't happen. Instead, the roilin' crowds snap some a' the ropes leadin' to the main center pole, and the huge tent starts to heave about like a giant bowl of Lutheran church women's Jell-O.

Then things git worse, cuz at the peak a' the ruckus the big pole bends like a wishbone and snaps. And now the whole tent starts t' collapse, as the air trapped inside slowly exhales through the little doors like a big dyin' blow-fish breathin' its last.

Well, Ole realizes right off how it's 92 per cent certain that 100 per cent a' the 220,000 souls inside that tent is on the verge of immediate extinction. Kwick as light, he turns t' Paul and sez they need a master plan fer savin' ev'ryone. And then the big Swede sits right down to think it through. He sez it shouldn't take more than two or three days to cum up with somethin'.

This relieves Ol' Paul of any legal responsibility, uv course, and he's glad a' that. But then— whilst Paul is just standin' tall in the center of the tent waitin' fer instructions frum Ole—the whole darn thing collapses down on his shoulders. Paul stretches out his long, strong arms t' hold it up, and not knowin' whut t' do next (cuz Ole ain't thunk that far yet), he whistles to Babe fer help.

Right quick, the Mighty Ox comes a'runnin', and uses his powerful horns to rip a long gash in the side a' the tent, so's ev'ryone kin escape. *And darned if they don't!* Throngs a' people cum swarmin' out a' that tent, cheerin' and screamin', and feelin' so relieved that they's huggin' ev'ryone in sight. Unforchoonately, once ev'ryone is safe outside, they realize Ole's still sittin' inside the tent. And they's all so curious to see how the master plan is comin', they run right back inside to watch him think.

Meanwhile, outside the tent the troll is now in total panic—and he's runnin' around in a big circle tryin' to escape, but gittin' nowheres fast. And back inside, Paul's still standin' there with outstretched arms. He's been thinkin' all the while, and he's decided he hates trolls. In fact, the more Paul thinks the madder he gits! Finally, he's so dad-blasted mad that he can't control hisself no longer, so's he just hauls off and rips that tent to shreds.

Paul emerges into the kool night air, kussin' and snarlin' and grindin' his teeth. And now— standin' full tall and silhouetted against the yellow moon—yew kin see fer yerself how mad he is!

All t'gether now: *"How mad is he?"*

Why—Paul's so mad that on a scale uv 1-10 it ranks 10, and that's **Lumberjack mad!**

The sight of Ol' Paul towerin' above the trees un-nerves the troll. The little rascal scoots off into the woods and hides, but Paul's so dad-blamed roarin' mad he just starts eliminatin' them woods, rippin' out full-growed trees with his bare hands and piling 'em up like cordwood.

A' course, Ole by now is plum brain-fagged frum all that thinkin', so's he's takin' a fifteen minute break. But once he see's all that wood pilin' up, he knows it's time t' chuck that master plan and load the wagons. Ole gathers the men and yokes the oxen.

"Gee haw," he yells.

Well, them oxen look at each other kinda puzzled-like, but then they haul them logs straight to the river, where they is floated downstream to the mills and sawed into boards, and the whole city of Duluth is built!

Still, Paul continues to rip, and Ole and the men continue to load the wagons.

"Haw gee," yells Ole, and once again those bewildered oxen find their way to the river, some-how. More logs is floated to the mill and stripped and squared—followin' which they's turned into railroad ties, and more'n 10,000 miles a' Great Northern track is laid!

"Haw gee haw," yells Ole—and so it goes. This time the logs is turned into toothpicks (by usin' some mysterious machine that nobudy under-stands), and 72,000,000,444 is boxed. In fact, not one toothpick has been made ever since, as we're still usin' 'em up to this very day!

Then—on the barren land where Paul has ripped out all them trees, Ole picks up a reddish rock.

"By golly if dis ain't iron ore!" he sez, and the great Mesabi Iron Range is discovered!

But Paul still don't stop. Night and day he keeps on relentlessly a-rippin' until—finally—he finds the humiliated little one-armed runt hisself, all huddled up and shakin' like a young man on his first date. Reachin' down, Paul snatches up that sorry critter and holds him scrunched inside his fist, so's only his head and his one good arm is showin'.

"This here's *yer* fault, yew scum-faced runt," Paul roars. "I'll squish yew like a grape!"

"No-nn-n-nnnooooooooo. Wait!" begs the troll, who now has to think real kwick, cuz he knows he's

Ole discoverin' Iron Ore at Mesabi

pleading fer his life. "Y-y-yoooou got it all wrong. I-It ain't even true that I's a t-t-troll."

"Not a troll?" sez Paul, seemin' suddenly somewhut puzzled. "But Ole sez..."

"Well—uh—folks—they sometimes just think I'm a troll cuz I'm small," sez the little rascal, whose mind is racin' desperate fast. "B-but akshully—uh—my name is—uh—Thumb! Yes— that's it! Gen'ral T-T-Tom Thumb. And it's a fact fer shure that I work fer P-T-T-T-T-T-T-T-T-T Barnum!"

Paul scratches his head, clearly confused. Then he grins. "Well, I'll be durned," sez he, forgettin' his anger. "It's the little gen'ral hisself. I's heard a' yew, and now I must say that it's a fine pleasure t' meet yew! Dang'd if I know why that fool Swede thunk yew wuz a troll."

Ol' Paul then leans over and sets that troll down gently on the ground. The little guy is sweatin' profusely, and close to passin' out.

"P-P-Please, Sir—would yew m-m-mind m-much if I m-m-mosey yonder t' that little house with the crescent m-m-moon on the door?" he asks, holdin' his little krotch with his one full sized hand. "All this excitement's been jest a m-m-mite m-m-much fer m-m-me."

Paul nods and grins, and the little guy scoots off.

"Cute li'l feller," winks Paul. "If it turns out he's a free agent, maybe we could sign him up t' be our camp mascot."

But a' course that's the last time he ever see'd that troll. Later on, Paul and Ole had many good-natured arguments concernin' the small guy. Ole always maintained it wuz a troll, but Ol' Paul never did believe in such kritters. To his dyin' day, Paul thunk he'd akshully met Gen'ral Tom Thumb.

Anyways—as yew may have guessed, the arm-wrestlin' contest wuz canceled that year. And since Ole left fer Minneap'lis a little later, the showdown match betwixt him 'n Paul never happened. In my opinion, that's probably just as well, cuz anyone who's a legend—like a Paul or an Ole— should never be a loser.

In fact, this way folks kin still argue about who woulda won—Big Ole or Ol' Paul. *And they do! They argue to this very day!* Like me fer example. There's no doubt in my mind who the champion woulda been! And I s'ppose yew have to have yer opinion too.

But—hey! I guess we can't never know fer sure!

Ole On Snoose Boulevard

That fateful day when Ole bid farewell to his good friend Paul wuz a bleak 'n gloomy one fer sure. Paul wuz sad, and Ole too, and as fer Babe—the Big Blue Ox shed a tear so large that it becum lake number 10,001 on Minnesoty's offishul list.

"Don't yew fergit we're gonna lock arms some day, and have that showdown," winked Paul, grinnin' frum inside his beard.

"Fer shure," sez Ole, whilst forcin' a bit uv a grin hisself.

So Ole waved g'bye then, and headed south. And this time he aimed hisself straight at the grandest and most fabulous city in all a' Minnesoty, which a' course wuz Minneap'lis.

In those days, Skandinavians arrivin' at this great thrivin' midwestern boomtown often chose t' settle down in the "Seven Korners District,"—a neighborhood perched high on the bluffs above the Missussipi, cross-river frum that there cute new little yooniversity skool. Skandinavians—bein' a sooperstitious lot—flocked t' live there cuz they thunk that seven wuz bound to mean good luck. But Skandinavians don't like t' talk about good luck stuff much, fer fear it might turn bad. So's any time folks asked 'em whereabouts in Minneap'lis they lived, they'd just mumble, and sometimes they'd not even answer. Thus started the myth that Skandinavians wuz a stoic lot, who never talked much.[5]

Anyways, Seven Korners in them days wuz best described as a melting pot, where Swedes and Norse and even a Dane or two all learned to live t'gether like one big family. That is, they acted totally dysfunctional, and fought a lot.

Big Ole fit right in, even though he had no idea whut dysfunctional meant. He took a second floor room above a little store called Samuelson's, and settled down.

Ole soon diskovered that the owner had a studio in the back, where he wuz teachin' tobaccy spittin' as a martial art. Well, the big Swede had such natural talent—and plus he'd spent years honing his skills—that it warn't long before he'd earned a black belt. Ole then went on to new heights, 'til by and by he becum known and rekognized as "Big Spit"—the offishul supreme champion uv the whole area.

And what d'ya know—after that, the Seven Korners District wuz renamed "Snoose Boulevard" in Ole's honor! Ev'ryone liked that a lot, a' course, cuz then they could finally speak up and tell folks where they lived. In fact,

[5] Anyone who thinks Skandinavians don't talk much oughta meet my wife!

tobaccy chewin' caught on big time with the menfolk after that (and with some a' the women folk, too), and to this day it remains almost as popular as lutefisk.

Then too, a' course, durin' Ole's Snoose Boulevard days inventions kept poppin' up inside his skull like ducks in a shootin' gallery! And some a' the ones worth listing at this point include—

(1) Ole's Pre-Chewed Snoose, fer people with no teeth.
(2) Ole's Coin Laundromats, fer washin' yer coins.
(3) Ole's new insurance plan called "My Fault Insurance,"
        and...
(4) Ole's Wood Stoves, made of Norway pine and guaranteed to burn at least four hours.

"Yah," sez Ole. "Dis here Minneap'lis iss my kinda place, by golly. Yew betcha fer shure! It's *da city uv my dreams!"*

Ole's Mysterious Dream

But speakin' of dreams—at this point Ole had a strange dream, wherein he dreamed he saw the woman of his dreams. She wuz wild and blonde and available, and by golly if she warn't beckoning fer him to cum. Ole found that he wuz drawn to her like a moth to a flame.

But there wuz details up close that he hadn't noticed frum afar. Like she wuz—horror of horrors—a Norwegian!! And she vas freckle-faced and kross-eyed to boot, with a 'beauty mark' by her left nostril, that looked kinda like a extra nostril!

Ole awoke at 3:00 AM in a cold sweat, and shakin' frum head to foot.

"Dat vas more uv a nightmare den a dream," he confided to his friends the next day over a cup of egg coffee.

Ole's Mysterious Dream

"Dat voman—by golly she vas a plump one. She vas only 5 foot 2, vhich ain't too bad, except she veighed 297 pounds."

"But da vurst part," sez Ole, *"iss dat she vas vaitin' fer me vith a ball and chain!"*

Even so, Ole could not shake the thought of this extraordinary woman frum his brain. He tingled and broke out in large goosebumps whenever he thunk of her...

...cuz she had a figure that men would kill for!

PART TWO:
LITTLE LENA
THE LEGENDARY
NORSE BEAUTY

Lena Lucretia Larsson
A Legend In Her Own Time

Little Lena & her Ma
Aged 4 & 44, respectively

Chapter Four:
Lena, The Early Years

Lena Gets Born

Now, Ole wuz a Swede, but Lena wuz a mountain girl frum Telemark in southern Norway. Like Ole, she'd been a sizeable baby—even by Norwegian standards—weighin' in at 29 lb. 7 oz. Indeed, some say that her poor ma needed 13 weeks to rekover.

Lena As A Young Girl In Norway

Anyways—Lena wuz a chubby young 'un, and she grew up to be more chubbier than before. She stood only 5 foot two, and had them proverbial Norwegian eyes a' blue, but unforchoonately she popped the scales at three pounds shy of three hundred. Our lady wuz freckle-faced and flaxen-haired—and also a bit cross-eyed, with a rather large...uh..."beauty mark" by her left nostril. But there wuz a voluptuous, Rubenesque quality to her figure that caused grown men to melt faster than Popsicles in El Paso.

In other words, them curves of hers wuz all in the right places. Yee Haw! [1]

---

[1] Those of yew who likes things "politically correct" had best stop readin' right now!!!

Boy, I shure do hate to say it, but whut Lena had in bulk, she lacked in brains. Indeed, it wuz later said that Lena wuz as dumb as Ole wuz smart.

- One story goes that she had a IQ of only 53—*and that's when totaled with her two sisters!*
- Anuther sez that in her school years she failed ev'rything but hist'ry—*and she never took hist'ry!*
- Then too there's the time she wuz rushed t' the hospital with severe facial burns. It seems she wuz at this Halloween party, *and wuz bobbin' fer french fries!*
- And I also heard tell she got fired frum her job as a elevator operator, *cuz she couldn't learn the route!*

Yet, even though Lena's cranial vacuum bordered on bein' legendary, this somehow upped her appeal to all them frisky young bucks who pursued her. Indeed, there's those who said that Lena wuz <u>so</u> dumb...

All t'gether now: *"How dumb wuz she?"*

Lena wuz so dumb that all the boys fought constantly fer her hand, and (heh, heh) fer all of her other body parts as well!

Now, lest yew think that Lena wuz just anuther pretty face, let me tell yew that this girl had *talent!* In fact, she had not one but *three talents!* Count 'em yerself. She wuz—

    (1) a champion butter maker,
       (2) a snowshoe champion,
          ...and
           (3) a better than average leg wrestler to boot.

Yep, that's three fer shure!

Lena, The Butter Maker

Let's talk about the butter-makin' first. Lena got into that by accident. The truth is, she didn't even own a churn. But it seems our lady loved fresh air milk baths. So she'd drag her old cast iron tub out into the front yard, and fill it chin-deep with goat's milk, after which she'd shed her duds and lay in there naked as a jaybird, sloshin' around like a happy otter in the spring melt. Sometimes she'd feel espeshully playful, and then she'd twitter and laugh and yodel and even jump up and down in the milk. One such day, while she wuz actin' extra foolish and rambunctious, a strange thing happened. The milk in the tub *turned to butter!*

Well, the neighbor boys come runnin' right over to make sandwiches, a' course. And after lunch they wuz nice enough to pry her out—which warn't easy, seein's she wuz locked in solid. The leftovers wuz such a greasy mess that Lena wuz gonna feed it to the hogs. But then someone suggested she could maybe make a few bucks instead. They told her to cut the stuff into one pound slabs, wrap it in shiny tinfoil paper all dekorated with little red hearts, and sell it door-to-door as "Little Lena's Bath Butter!"

She did it, by gum, and danged if it warn't an instant sell-out. Ev'ry red-blooded Norwegian male fer miles about had t' have a pound or two!

Lena, The Snowshoe Champion And Leg Wrestler

Now, su'prising as it seems, Lena had more skills too. In a bleak northern nation like Norway where it snows an average of 11.5 months a year, folks somehow thrive on frigid pastimes such as skatin' and skiin' and snowshoein', and our chubby Norse miss wuz no excepshun. She wuz

Lena gits stuck
in the butter.

Ole & Lena

plenty good at all three, but her specialty wuz snowshoein'. In fact, Lena won lots a' gold medals, and wuz so proud that *she had 'em all bronzed!*

Yup, she wuz a kwick one. Folks wuz always amazed to see such a pudgy little rascal zippin' along so fast on snowshoes, but of course there wuz a reason. She got plenty a' praktice, yew see, *runnin' frum all them there wild-eyed young Norsky studs!*

Through such activities our lady developed great, powerful calves of steel, and becum skilled at leg wrestlin' too. After that, there warn't nary a soul in all a' Telemark nor out yonder over them mountains in any direktion who could beat her.

That Lena wuz tougher than Tilda Torgerson's ten-year-old toffee, I kid yew not!

Let's see, now. I already said that Lena wuz plump, and attraktive, and—uh—cranially challenged. I also listed her talents of buttermakin', snowshoein', and leg wrestlin'. But it seems like there wuz somethin' else too. Hmmmm. *Oh shure!* It's the fact that Lena wuz a wild one. Yew readers already know that, a' course, frum all them Ole and Lena jokes. And yew know too that I can't change the facts, neither. So's I'll admit right up front here that there's stories I'd rather leave outa this book! But as a dedicated historian, I'm stuck.

I gotta report things as they really wuz!

The truth is that Lena just warn't one a' them sedate, reserved, typikal Norwegians like yer used to seein' in church on Sunday. Frum the time she budded and blossomed and bloated into such a headstrong young lass, she knew how t' git things goin'. Riots and fist fights broke out wherever she went, and it often looked like a 5-day battle zone after she passed through.

I mean, this woman wuz a absolute embarrassment! She'd party and dance and hoot and holler and carry on 'til all hours of the night. And becuzza this, her fame spread far and wide, 'til she wuz just as famous as Ole hisself!—*but fer differ'nt reasons, a' course.*

So there yew have it, folks—that's Lena! And yew'd likely guess that someone with such a juicy hotdish of traits wuz bound to lead a high-flyin' adventurous life. But then, yer about to see all that fer yerselves, as we proceed now.

Lena Meets Edvard Grieg

So yew all heard of Edvard Grieg, I s'ppose. Uh—did someone say no? Well, fer those of yew who's not so cultured as the rest of us, I kin say that he wuz Norway's greatest composer. *Musik, yew know.* Duh!

Shurely yew know that he wrote that there Peer Gynt thing. *Right!* And a whole mess a' purty love songs, too.

Movin' right along then—do yew *really* think it wuz Grieg's beloved Nina who inspired him to write all that good stuff? That's whut those fudge-brained historians would have yew believe. But they is wrong again, as usual! Fer it wuz Lena (not Nina) who first uncorked his most highest octane musikal juices. But rather than tell yew myself how it all cum about, let me quote frum a factual essay writ by little Ingeborg Gilbertson of Belgrade, Minnesoty, the smartest girl in Miss Shirley Shipstead's 8th grade hist'ry class:

> Oh yah, that Edvard Grieg—darned if he warn't the first great luv a' Lena's life. The man wuz laid out under a tree one day, scratchin' hisself and twirlin' his big bushy mustache. He'd never writ much musik up 'til then—outside a' some extra verses fer "chopsticks"—but all of a sudden here comes Lena on her snowshoes. She wuz yodeling at the time—like she liked t' do—and good golly her stretch fer high B flat most nearly blowed his brain.

Ole & Lena

Edvard & Lena (Not Nina)

Well, that Grieg—he set right up and scowled, and he wuz about t' suggest she try A sharp instead. But then he looks her over, and he goes "Gulp," and then—darned if he don't hear chords and clefs and flats and stuff inside his skull like ones that nobudy ain't never heard before!

"Shazam!" sez he, and he sez "Cum," and then he drags her into his house and plunks her down on a chair, and then he plunks out them chords on his piano, and he writes 'em down and plays 'em back, and darned if they ain't trooly somethin' else!

And then that Lena—she gits all weepy cuz she thinks they's so gosh-durn purty.

Oh yah, that Lena—up 'til then she'd bin mostly into guys who wuz leg wrestlers. And that Grieg—well, he wuz such a thin little shrimp that he warn't never into such bestial physical activities. But once Lena heard them purty tunes, she commenced t' hang around his place a lot—like a horse thief on a gallows.

Well, that Lena—she liked t' call her devoted Edvard "my little Pumpkin Face," and sometimes she even called him "Edvardo," which he liked maybe just a little better than "my little Pumpkin Face." So a' course yew kin see frum all this, then, that we're talkin' luv at first sight fer both a' them two frisky Norskies.

Oh yah, that Grieg—he'd been dating Nina (not Lena) up 'til then. But then Nina warn't Lena, and once he'd met Lena, he gave Nina the boot.

"Uff da!" sez Nina. *"Yew yust kan't never trust dem musikal men!"*

That Grieg—I gotta tell yew he wuz plum crazy in luv with Lena (not Nina), so's he got all gushy.

"Oh joy," sez he. "Oh bliss! What rapture reigns when two such kindred souls unite! We're talkin'

happiness. We're talkin' insatiable passions. Yes—
we're talkin' major turn-ons that rank right up
there with... uh...herring soup, or...uh...maybe even
Hattie Hagstrom's Head Cheese Hot Dish!"

Oh yah, that Grieg—he liked t' call Lena (not
Nina) his little "gouda cheeseball." Poor Nina!
'Twas Lena who set his heart t' poundin' somethin'
awful. Well goodness gracious, don't yew know?
Whenever said heart got to thumpin' in three
quarter time, said composer got to stompin' said
feet to the beat uv said heart, and then he wuz
inspired to write said purty musik. And cross my
little schoolgirl heart and hope to die—*darned if
his goodest works warn't writ whenever said Lena
(not said Nina) sloshed about, makin' said butter
in said tub!*

I ask yew, dear reader, whoever yew are—who
could ever fergit the likes uv—

"Classy Lassy, Fat N' Sassy"

"Nickel Lena"

"The Snowshoe Polka"

"Have Yew Seen-a My Lena?"

"My Sweet Little Norsky Butterball"

Oh yah, that Grieg—once he hit the musikal
big time, darned it he warn't hot t' marry said Lena
(not Nina). And so he wooed her with flours, and
wowed her with choklates, and a' course he pro-
posed, and even give her a dime 'n ring!

But goodness gracious—sad to say—this union
just warn't meant to be! Cuz 'twas just one week
before the wedding that fickle Lena (not Nina) met
the great Norwegian painter, Leonardo duh
Vincison, and then it wuz—

"Good-bye Grieg!"

Alas, how the heartbroke composer grieved. But then—darned if he don't go crawlin' right back to Nina (not Lena), who he called his little "Veggie Dip." And since Nina (not Lena) liked all that gushy sweet talk stuff she forgived him, sorta, and they wuz married, and the whole gosh-darn thing wuz cleaned up later by all them stuffy, straight-laced historians.

A' course, once Nina'd (not Lena'd) becum Mrs. Grieg, she read Ed the riot act! And then she burned a whole bunch a' them purty luv songs he'd writ about Lena (not Nina). And don't yew know, the goners is amongst the best he ever did.[2] The End!

Anyways—lest yew have even the slightest doubts regardin' the truth of Miss Gilbertson's essay, I submit that it wuz graded A+ by her teacher. And darned it it warn't embellished with a hand drawn smiley face—though the teacher also added a note which read—

"Watch yer spellin'."

The Mona Lena

Well, Lena's second great love wuz the brilliant Norwegian painter, Leonardo duh Vincison. Their legendary romance commenced when Lena cum t' Oslo fer the annual Norwegian Snowshoe Championships. And there she wuz spotted by this greatest among greats as she sat downtown in the Grand Hotel, sippin' on a chocolate lutefisk soda.

---

[2] Forchoonately, the great Nickel Lena has survived, but the long-lost Snowshoe Polka wuz even greater. Some musikal experts have told me that it ranked right up there with Beethoven's Tenth or Eleventh Symphony.

It wuz as if the heavens opened fer the magnificent Leonardo! Quicker than instant oatmeal, he fell madly in love with her. Ah yes, he wuz inspired to paint—and he knew at once that he'd know no peace unless he posed this perfectly portentous possessor of plump, palpitating pulchritude fer his greatest masterpiece, the <u>Mona Lena</u>!

Now, Lena's first impulse wuz to turn him down, her bein' such a shy lass (she sez), not given to show. *But then again, it's not ev'ry day that a girl frum Telemark gits t' be immortalized!*

Leonardo had first planned that the painting be a nude! But forchoonately this awful scandal wuz avoided, since his studio wuz unheated. In fact, Lena had to pose in a hooded goose-down parka and big furry mittens, her face covered with a hand-knit Norwegian ski mask. The final result wuz certainly no candidate fer the Playboy Magazine. Nevertheless, the painting caused a instant sensation.

"It leaves more to the imagination," stated the artist.

Once done, the <u>Mona Lena</u> wuz unveiled in a gala midsummer's day ceremony at the "Museum of Great Norwegian Art," in downtown Oslo. Bein' the first and only painting in the museum, it wuz such a hot smash hit that throngs a' parka-clad persons stood in long lines outside the building fer hours, fightin' off packs of starvin' wolves in a raging blizzard, just t' see it.

Whut D'ya Know, It's Lars Again

Meanwhile, Lars Alva Eddyson wuz dressed in rags and livin' in frozen poverty on Oslo's Skid Row (yew may recall that he'd slunk off t' Norway after losin' all his money in Amerika). Anyways—one day Lars wuz standin' in line at the museum, thinkin' it's a soup line, and he sees

Leonardo painting the
Mona Lena

Note: Our lady has removed her
ski mask briefly, whilst Leo
puts the finishin' touches on the
Mona Lena's inscrutable smile.

the great painting of the lovely Lena. Instantly, that grungy bum falls madly in love with her, as had Edvardo and Leonardo before him.

After that, Lars wuz obsessed. He thunk about her day and night. He couldn't concentrate. Fer shure he couldn't sleep. Finally, in fog-brained desperation he tracked her down, and tried t' court her. But Lena thunk that constipated twerp wuz *way too smart* fer her taste!— and so she spurned ev'ry last one a' his aggravatin' amorous advances.

Nevertheless, it wuz then that the thievin' slimeball come up with his last great invention—*biodegradable paintings*—which is here discussed in a three pound book on art hist'ry writ by his gran'son, the well-known Professor Teddy Eddyson—[3]

It seems that biodegradability was not well understood in Lena's time. Years later, chemists learned that *oil paints mixed with cornstarch would gradually decompose when exposed to sunlight!* But that phenomenon was not known in 19th century Norway.

Grandpa Lars was visiting the duh Vincison studio in downtown Oslo, when he was blessed with a brilliant flash of inspiration.

"EUREKA!" he cried out, unexpectedly.

Then, turning to Leonardo, he told the artist to add a pinch of cornstarch to each of his palette paints. It was a stroke of purest genius, now recognized as a turning point in the history of Norwegian art.

"But who would want cornstarch paintings?" asked the puzzled artist.

---

[3] By the way, I'm usin' these quotes without permission, so don't tell anybody.

"Just do it," said grandpa Lars, "It's a new genre, and you shall be its master!"

"Besides that," he added in a hushed voice, *"your paintings will all disintegrate after about a month, and then you can collect the insurance."*

The grateful artist then used these starched pigments to complete a second profound masterpiece, the <u>Lena de Milo</u>.

Anyways, that's the story the way Lars told it to his gran'son. But somehow the same story comes out differ'nt when Leo tells it. Here's whut it sez in the artist's journal, fer the entry uv September 7—

Dearest Diary: *(it sez)*

I was working on the <u>Lena de Milo</u> today, and the lovely and gentle Lena was posing for it sans arms, when the door to my studio burst open. It was that dang fool Lars Eddyson again. He was acting like a babbling lunatic, frothing at the mouth and chasing Lena all over the room.

"Cum to me, my little poopsie," he shrieked with crazed emotion, casting chairs and tables aside. "Cum to Papa!"

Finally, Lena'd had enough.

"That's it, frog-face," she yelled—and turning suddenly she hauled off and smacked him so hard that he staggered backwards, knocking a bowl of cornstarch onto my palette. I later noticed that this gave the oils an odd consistency, and I was moved to use them to complete my painting.

Anuther entry dated October 7 continues the story—

Dearest Diary: *(it sez again)*

Exactly one month has passed since I completed the <u>Lena de Milo,</u> and today I was shocked to find that the painting has disintegrated into a cone-shaped pile of cornstarch dust. At first I was upset, but then I realized that painting in this medium could make me rich. It would generate lots of repeat business, as *my customers would periodically have to replace their paintings!*

A' course, anyone who's up on things knows that Leonardo went on to becum the greatest master of the biodegradable medium! He also founded the "Painting of the Month Club," which turned out to be one swell koncept fer all koncerned, *since no one wanted t' look at his paintings fer more than a month, anyways!*

Alas, none a' Leonardo's paintings survive. They wuz all done with cornstarch paints except fer the <u>Mona Lena</u>, and that one wuz stole by some sneaky rotten low-down thief on the very night when that sneaky rotten low-down Lars Eddyson vanished forever. And neither Eddyson or the <u>Mona Lena</u> ain't never been heard frum, ever since.

Today, Oslo's "Museum of Great Norwegian Art" has three galleries filled with piles a' cornstarch dust, and long lines of Norwegians file past 'em daily, in respektful silence. Of course, no one outside a' Norway ever got t' see no Leonardic stuff fer theirselves, so's yew just have t' believe it when Norwegians tell yew how great he wuz.

Nevertheless, yew may rest assured that Leonardo's reputashun as one a' the world's all-time greatest artists is secure—

since ev'ryone knows that Norwegians don't lie!

Lena at the
North Pole!

Chapter Five:
Lena's Big Trek To Amerika

(or, Headin' to Wiskonsin,
With Stops Along the Way)

Well, Leonardo vanished one day, and no one seems to know whut becum of him, exactly. Some say he got cornstarch paint on hisself and disintegrated along with his paintings. And Professor Teddy Eddyson reports that a super-sized pile a' cornstarch dust wuz found in his studio back then.

So Lena felt kinda lost, since a pile a' cornstarch ain't none too cuddly—plus she'd lost her modelin' job besides. And so—having been immortalized in Norwegian song and paint—she thunk it might be fun to seek out new adventures in Amerika. Her trip wuz a spur a' the moment thing, cuz ev'rything that Lena did wuz kinda wild and spontaneous, and almost never planned out too good. She decided t' save time by takin' the short cut right over the top a' the globe, on her snowshoes.

During this trek, she survived on melted snow and dried lutefisk as she trudged on through savage Arctic storms and fought off hungry polar bears with her bare hands. Along the way, she met Fridtjof Nansen—the great Norwegian Arctic explorer—trekkin' about aimlessly in the snowy wilderness, as he wuz prone to do. The poor soul wuz lost as a chord, and he shure wuz happy t' meet Lena, cuz she told him how to find his way back home.

No doubt, he woulda been even happier if her direktions had been right!

Whatever.

Anyways—Lena pulled in at the North Pole, which she rekognized right off, since it looked kinda like a big stripey barber pole stickin' up outa the snow.

"I vas kinda hopin' somebody'd be here too tell me vich vay vas south," she sez, kinda disappointed-like, not knowin' a' course that she wuz the first person who'd ever been there.

A violent blizzard wuz ragin' at the time. Even so, Lena took time to stand at attenshun and yodel the <u>Norwegian Nash'nul Anthem</u>, plus too she tossed in a couple a' verses frum <u>Nickel Lena,</u> just fer the heck of it. Two hungry tone-deaf polar bears attacked her halfways through the chorus, but she drop kicked 'em both with her powerful legs, and sent 'em sprawlin'.

Them bears took off, and Lena decided t' follow. And so—continuin' relentlessly on down through uncharted polar regions in sub-zero weather, Lena snowshoed over giant ice floes by day, and swum through icy waters by night, dodgin' star-lit killer icebergs while she went.

Now—all a' this is epic adventure at its absolute finest, and I know yew'll agree that if it ever becum a Hollywood movie, it'd star Dolly Parton, and she'd win the Oskar fer shure.

Well, them bears gave Lena the slip somewheres in upper Canada, after which she wandered aimlessly fer days on end in waist-deep snow, not knowin' where she wuz. Then—suddenly—outa nowheres cums a couple a' elderly Eskimos wadin' towards her.

"Oo seeda ugalee-pooku, gwab du-wooky porky dork. Hoohoo!" sez one.

"And a howdy-doo to yew, too," sez Lena.

It's indeed fortunate that those Eskimos knew how to write, cuz they later recorded the details of this enkounter in a sealskin diary, which I diskovered just last spring while browsing in the archives of the Hudson Bayou Company during my lunch hour. I shall now quote frum that diary, regardin' whut happened next—

"Ohno plump dweeb apuku dot com. Googla whapoo snooshoo Lena! Tuuna gwib dumb Norske, bumgolly! Coo-coo dubl ugalee wuuk. Uff da! Wump-wump inook—da bigrump too. Woof woof. Hoo haw! Dang snooker dum gullible wump? Hoohoo! Gumba map ting blub wiichiinook ooo bath inook oo butter! Zonk tong whapu twix bar. Moo moo. Heehee! Whoopee!"

Well, akshully, there's a whole lot more to it than that. *It just goes on and on!* But to make a long story short—

(1) After fierce dickerin', Lena trades three pounds a' frozen bath butter to them Eskimos fer a map!
(2) On that map there's a big red dot that sez "Noo York City!"
(3) Lena thinks it's fruit, and asks 'em how to git t' that Big Apple!
(4) Them Eskimos just flash her a pair of toothless grins, and shrug their shoulders and point out across Hudson Bayou!!
(5) After more fierce dickerin', Lena trades 'em her last pound a' bath butter fer a vintage kayak, after which she paddles off across the Bayou!
(6) She then paddles south along the river system towards the Yew-Ess-of-A!
(7) Unfortunately, all this is against the current, so she has to *shoot all the rapids in reverse!!*

Lena Meets Rocky Feller

Uff da! That wuz one tough trek fer shure, as yew kin tell frum all them exclamation marks! But Lena finally got to Amerika, by golly. Then, seein's how she liked excitement, she bee-lined it straight to Noo York City in gen'ral, and Times Square in pertikyoolar. And a' course she joined right in with that disgusting creepy crowd, who wuz always hangin' out down there hootin' and hollerin' and dancin' and partyin' and actin' weird 'til all hours a' the night.[1]

Good grief—*whatever!*

Anyways, it wuz at Times Square, then, whilst minglin' in one a' them late-night New Year's eve crowds, that she met this nice young gent named Rocky Feller (or some such thing). And they becum good friends right off, cuz—like the old sayin' goes—opposites attract. Lena later said that outside a' Lars Eddyson, Rocky wuz no doubt the smartest man she'd ever met.

And as fer Rocky, he later said that Lena wuz—well—about as bright as a broken bulb.

But the fact that Lena wuz so dumb warn't all that bad, sez Rocky, cuz at least she wuz "consistent." That is, she wuz consistently *wrong!* In fact, Rocky cum t' value her advice far above anyone else's, becuz—as he remembered later in life, "That Lena was <u>so</u> dumb..."

All t'gether now: *"How dumb wuz she?"*

"That Lena was <u>so</u> dumb that whatever she recommended was bound to be wrong! So whatever she said, I did just the opposite!"

Fer example! Rocky wuz just commencin' with his life back then, and he couldn't decide whut he should do with it.

"Lena," sez he, "what do you think? Should I pursue the oil business, or should I become a short order cook in south Brooklyn?"

Well, our lady didn't see much future in oil (seein' as Henry Fjord had not yet got around to inventin' automobiles), so she went with the cook choice. That settled it fer Rocky, who quickly opted fer oil.

Next, Rocky had to choose betwixt buyin' some dirt-cheap land way down in Texas, or usin' that same money

---

[1] We're talkin' very un-Norwegian-like behavior, to say the least.

Rocky Feller & Friend

t' take Lena to a big, gala Jenny Lind concert down on Broadway.

"Vell, I shure vould like to hear dat Lind lady sing!" sez Lena. "And as fer buyin' dat dere vorthless land—yew'd yust haff too pay taxes on it."

A' course, that wuz Rocky's cue to buy the land, and it warn't more'n a few hours 'til oil wuz diskovered there. After that, things took off faster than killer bees after a honey thief. Rocky wuz soon waist-deep in cash and chin-deep in his books, actin' oblivious, and devotin' night and day to his bus'ness. Lena tried t' snap him out of it.

"Cum on, Rocky-Pooh," she pleaded. "If yew seen one barrel, yew seen 'em oil! Let's go have fun"

But Rocky wuz too busy calculatin' his profits to respond.

Years later, Rocky looked up frum his ledgers one day. He'd made millions by then, and he called out fer Lena.

"Git dressed, darlin'," sez he. "I'll take you to that Jenny Lind concert now." But Lena warn't nowheres to be found.

Well, Rocky wuz flat-out stunned once he realized his lady wuz gone. And frum that day on, he just couldn't git her off his mind. Inside his skull she becum the main obsession—bigger than oil, even! Some sources say that Rocky wanted to call his big new building the "Little Lena Center," but got overruled by his own board a' direktors. They insisted on callin' it the *"Rocky Feller Center!"*

Other sources say it wuz ditto fer the Rockettes. Yep, Rocky wanted to call 'em the *"Little Lenettes!"*

As the years passed by, Rocky spent gobs a' oil-smeared cash tryin' to find his Lena again. *In fact, yer author thinks he kin still remember, as a young man, seein' a milk carton with Lena's picture on it.* But sad to say, it wuz all fer naught—and her memory haunted him to his dyin' day.

Lena Hits Rock Bottom

Well, Lena had left Noo York City, a' course, and the next thing she'd done wuz snowshoe on down to Phillydelfya—even though it happened t' be July. And it wuz there—while tryin' to forget Rocky and his oil—that she hit rock bottom.

By now, a' course yew know all about our lady's rash and rowdy ways, and I s'ppose yer thinkin' that sooner or later she'd outgrow all that. But sad t' say, things wuz predestined to git lots worse before they got better.

Fer shure!

So now—at the risk of trashin' our lady's reputation completely, I must next delve into her compulsion t' hang out in Phillydelfya's vilest and most raunchiest saloons. And I mean we're talkin' pure sleaze—crowded, noisy joints with dim lights, and foul-smellin' cheap whisky, and pool playin', and worse.[2] Dang it all—I shure do hate to grovel in the garbage, but then this *is* a hist'ry book, and *facts is facts!*

Our lady loved to dance, and late one night at a disgusting unlicensed smoke-filled shack called Archie's Bunker she wuz doin' a lively leg-bending dance of her own creation, called the "Lutefisk Stomp." To the musik of a honky-tonk piano and amid hoots and hollers, she'd stomped her way right up on top a' the bar, snowshoes and all—and plus she wuz doin' her own sleazy impression of Eve and the apple—when one a' the patrons made a pass at her. Followed her right up on top a' the bar, he did. Yessir—he wrestled her down, and nailed her right on the lips with a big wet unsolicited smooch.

---

[2] I'll say it again. We're talkin' <u>very</u> un-Norwegian-like behavior!

Now, if ever there wuz a woman who wuz skilled in the fine art of persuasion, it wuz Lena. She knew just how to reason with any man who tried t' touch without permission. In this case, she yanked off one snowshoe and whopped him so hard that he wuz out 'til breakfast.

Well, this disgruntled gent—bein' Irish, and high-strung (and far frum sober to boot, I might add)—almost popped a artery over the abrupt manner in which she'd spurned his amorous advances.

"No more Mr. Nice Guy!" sez he. "I'm gonna take that soup-brained, snowshoein' Norsky t' court, and *sue her pants off fer sexual harassment!*"

Lena Meets Susan B. Anthony

Now, normally a disgusting incident like this is best fergot, I s'ppose. I mention it only cuz these wuz the sordid cirkumstances whut brung Lena t'gether with that most famous of all crusadin' women's rights activists, Susan B. Anthony—or "Suzy B," as Lena called her.

The followin' Pyoolitzer Prize winnin' story frum the front page a' the Phillydelfya Enquirer describes the trial, and also tells how Sue and Lena cum t' be best friends:

News Flash: Phillydelfya: Lena Larsson—also known as the "Wild Woman of Telemark"—was being defended by the crack legal team of Dewey, Cheetum, and Howe. They'd retained Ms. Anthony as an expert witness, and the courtroom was packed to the rafters, since this was expected to be a landmark case in the history of women's rights.

Crusader Sue entered the courtroom. She was a bun-haired woman with undersized spectacles pinched to her nose. And her favorite color must have been black, as she was wearing it from head to toe.

"I shure iss pleased too meet yew, Reverend Father," said Lena, before she realized her mistake. But Ms. Anthony seemed not to notice, as she was busy conversing with us reporters.

The lady in black took the stand, and her testimony (yawn) dragged on for hours. Lena could tell that Ms. Anthony was probably scoring a few points, but she saw too that both judge and jury were (yawn) on the verge of going to sleep. Moreover, during cross-examination the plaintiff's attorney droned on and on and (yawn) and on.

"Surely, Ms. Anthony, you can see that *your* devious client, Lena, first provoked *my* poor defenseless client to act, and then she (yawn) walloped him. Certainly you'd agree that this was an act of pure malicious (yawn) felony aggression, was it not?"

Well, Lena'd finally had enough! Before Ms. Sue could answer, she leaped right up onto the judge's bench.

"I'll show yew vut I vas doin', Yudgey-Pooh, so's yew kin c fer yerself dat it varn't nuttin' prowocative. *I vas yust bein' me!*"

So said, she donned her snowshoes and started doing the Lutefisk Stomp right up there under the judge's nose.

Words simply cannot describe the wanton chaos that followed! The judge went berserk and so did the lawyers. They all scrambled up on top of the bench with Lena, wrestled her down, and tried for a smooch. Lena was fighting them off, snowshoes in hand. Flashbulbs were popping, and we reporters were going wild. The bailiffs finally subdued the judge and the lawyers, and dragged them yelling and screaming from the courtroom.

Ole & Lena

Susan B. Anthony
testifyin' before the judge

So the judge and those lawyers all spent the night in jail. All charges against Lena were dropped, and pictures of both her and Ms. Anthony were plastered all over the front pages of newspapers nationwide.

Well, Sue thunk it wuz the best publicity ever fer her cause, and I might add that those two were bosom buddies ever since. *(Whoops—scratch that, 'cause we can't have bosoms in a women's rights story!)*

Sue And Lena Trade Life Styles

Anyways—Sue and Lena wuz not exactly whut yew'd call "two peas in a pod." Suzy B had little use fer the men, and early on she concluded that if yew don't look like a woman, yew shure won't be treated like one.

Then too, she didn't like women bein' boy toys, and so she insisted that Lena change her ways. Whut d'ya know, our lady wuz *so* dumb...

All t'gether now: *"How dumb wuz she?"*

Our Lena wuz so dumb that she believed ol' Sue, when she told her it just warn't very lady-like to be so attractive!

And so it wuz that Lena learned all about usin' bloomers and hair buns and big words and such.

But now, folks, it's time fer anuther one a' them hardly-known historical facts. Did yew ever wonder how Ms. Anthony got all them funds to support her cause? Well, accordin' to rekords I unearthed whilst researchin' this book, there wuz akshully two sources fer her income:

(1) First, that lady in black wuz smart enough t' know that Lena wuz hot. Whut she had wuz sure to sell—bigtime—and Ol' Sue knew it. So she started stealin' Lena's beauty secrets on the side, makin' a list and checkin' it twice.

In time, she wrote up them secrets in a "Dew It Yerself" book, published it anonymous, and made herself a dumpster full a' cash.

(2) But hey, there's more too. Them rekords show how Sue went further still in exploitin' whut she learned frum Lena. Namely, she had *a second, secret identity!* Five days a week she wuz the stern and staid old Susan B. Anthony that yew all know frum yer women's lib books. But git this, folks! On weekends she'd sneak off and assume her alter-identity of a side show dancer known as "Little Egypt!"

And them bucks flowed in like water frum a hose, cuz her show-stopper wuz none other than *the Lutefisk Stomp!!!*

So yew kin see that if it warn't fer Lena, the whole women's rights movement woulda never got off the ground, and all yew women readers would still be persecuted somethin' awful by us men. And so, ladies, instead a' bein' so downright critical of Lena all the time, *yew should thank yer lucky stars that she wuz whut she wuz!*

Lena At The Circus

Well, Lena warn't the type whut could be tied up in buns and bloomers fer very long. In time, she parted ways with her good pal Sue, after which she breathed one big sigh a' relief and reverted to her disgusting ol' trash-kickin' ways. Just lately, she'd heard tales of the wild west, with its cowboys and Indians and foul-smellin' gunslingers and free-spirited women and drinkin' and card-playin' and such—and it sounded like her kinda place.

"Yippee ki-yi, git along little dogie!" she sez, donning a ten gallon hat. And then she headed west, like so many a immigrant before her. Lena traveled by boat along the

Erie Canal and on through them great lakes. A' course, her kustom of wearin' snowshoes on the boat raised quite a stir, causin' all them petite little society gals to turn up their petite little noses (and watch their petite little toes) whenever she wuz around.

After dockin' at Milwuckey, Lena continued on west, hitchin' wagon rides until she arrived at the wild west town a' Baraboo, Wiskonsin. Well—akshully—Baraboo wuz not exactly Tombstone, but it did have the circus. Cuz Baraboo, my friends, wuz the home town of them five Ringling Brothers[3] and their big new travelin' tent show.

Lena spent some time there with them Ringling boys, and according to the uncensored memoirs of Cuckoo the Clown, her interdukshun to the circus come about like this—

By golly—that's a day I'll never fergit. It wuz circus time!—and inside the big top the action wuz on.

"Ladies and gentlemen and children of all ages," cried the Ringmaster. "Your attention please!"

And all through the tent, every eye wuz fixed on Almonzo, the world's greatest trapeze artist. Yes—the drums wuz a-rollin' and the crowd wuz a-gaspin', cuz this wuz the exact moment when Almonzo comes flyin' through the air towards the arms of the catcher. *Unfortunately, it wuz also the exact moment that Lena walked into the big top.*

Well, all them eyes immediately blinked and turned towards Lena, including those of the catcher, who—momentarily stunned by the sudden sight of plentiful, pale, pulsating, passionate Norwegian flesh—missed completely.

---

[3] We're talkin' Albert, Otto, Alfred, Charles, and John. Check it out. I think that's five.

Lena and Cuckoo
in a friendly pose

The great Almonzo crashed headlong through the roof a' the lion cage, where he landed on the big cat's back, and—well, yew don't want to hear the rest.

Fer shure!

Anyways—by the time they'd cleaned up the mess and calmed down the crowd, Lena wuz nowheres to be found. She'd sauntered on down to the next tent, where us clowns wuz prakticing, and she joined right in. When John Ringling stopped by, she wuz teachin' us this quaint Norwegian folk dance called the Lutefisk Stomp—a dance that has some real provocative bone-bending moves, to say the least!

Well, John wuz so impressed that he hired Lena right on the spot, to help us clowns improve our acts. And later on, he tried long and hard to sign her up as a dancer in his travelin' tent show.

"We'd team you with our star headline dancer, whom we call *Little Egypt*," he said hopefully, "and you would be called...*Little Norway!*"

Well, Lena politely declined the dance team offer. She preferred workin' with us clowns, she said, cuz we reminded her so much of her family. And many of them classic clown skits which wuz developed during Lena's circus stay is used by clowns ev'rywheres to this very day.

But Lena never thought of them skits as bein' funny, a' course. She said she wuz just preserving her ethnic heritage, *cuz that's whut life back there in Norway wuz really like!*

A' course, there's a footnote to Cuckoo's story, and perhaps yew picked up on it already. Namely, *Little Egypt wuz akshully Lena's old pal, Suzy B—although Lena never knew it.*

Them Wiskonsin Cheeze Heads

Well, durin' her stay in boomin' Baraboo, Lena helped support herself by opening up a little shop down by the river, that she called "Little Lena's Circus World Bath Butter Boutique." She made her butter whilst bathin' out back and sold it up front.[4] Not long later, she enlarged her product line to include *Lena's Limburger Cheeze.* We won't delve into the rank details of that one, excep' to say that it wuz the start of the whole Wiskonsin cheeze industry.

But of course nuthin' ever goes good fer very long in Wiskonsin. Lena found things going downhill downright fast after some a' the lokal down-home rednecks started hangin' out down at her shop. It wuz a downer the way they'd stop in down there to gab and gawk and down the Limburger. Finally, Lena got downright mad!

"Git outa here and leave me alone, yew down-dumb hick Wiskonsin *cheeze heads,*" she hollered, turnin' red as a cow barn. She meant it as a put-down, a' course, but them down-and-out dummies wuz too downright dense to know up frum down!

Well—wouldn't yew know, them down-and-dirty rednecks akshully liked bein' called cheeze heads—and that's whut they's called theirselves ever since. In fact, things got downright worse, cuz it spurred 'em on. Why, they'd take big pie-shaped bricks of Lena's Limburger, balance 'em on their heads, and run all around the downtown square, hootin' and hollerin' and smellin' somethin' awful! Of course, that's the way Wiskonsin folks is to this very day—as kin be seen at any Green Bay Packers football game. And Wiskonsin folks bein' who they are, I doubt they'll ever change.

---

[4] Plant tours where yew could akshully see the butter bein' made wuz popular. Espeshully with the men folk.

As fer Lena, she'd had it with Wiskonsin.

"Fer shure!" she said. "I kan't stand all dat *badgering!"*

And so she reckoned it wuz time to leave them cheeze heads behind, and continue trekkin' toward that great flat western horizon. Out there yonder—amidst cacti and yucca and bison and rattlesnakes, bathed in the reddish light of the setting sun—there lay the legendary wild west frontier a-beckoning.

Lena's Ideal Man

Now, the way Lena wuz avoidin' the gent-folks of late, yew might think she'd been brainwashed by Suzy B to the point where she'd lost all interest in the opposite sex. But hey—that just ain't true! In fact, yer about t' learn there wuz a whole 'nother side to Lena. 'Twas many a mournful, moonlit night that our lady laid wide-eyed awake in her bed, all alone 'n thinkin' of her "dream man." And this wuz one girl who knew *exactly* whut she wanted. The man of Lena's dreams would have to be many things—

(1) He'd have to be big! So all-fired big that she would seem petite by komparison. Indeed, *Lena wuz totally turned on by men who weighed exactly 444 pounds.*[5]

(2) The man of Lena's dreams would also have to be smarter than her! *(But then that warn't too hard a thing, since ev'ryone wuz).*

(3) And finally (this bein' the most important of all), *her dream man would have to be able to beat her 3 outa 4 in leg wrestlin'!*

[5] Remember back there in Chapter One? That's whut Ole weighed! Yep.

Lena Meets Wild Bill Hiccup

Still lookin' fer the man of her dreams, Lena arrived by stagecoach at the rip-roarin', rough-'n-tumble frontier town of Deadwood, South Duckota. Though her stay there wuz brief, it's still remembered as one a' the most colorful episodes in the hist'ry of this most colorful of frontier towns. In fact, a few years ago the Deadwood Chamber of Commerce decided to publish a colorful brochure tellin' the factual story of Lena's stay in their historic hamlet. Now, I've heard tell that this brochure is kurrently outa print, and recent trav'lers report that them Chamber folks will sometimes deny it even exists. That's no doubt cuz they is so embarrassed about not havin' no more copies t' pass out. Forchoonately, I have in my possession a somewhut faded Xerox copy of one a' the originals, which I'll be happy t' share with yew at this time. It goes like this—

> Come along, folks! Return with us now to those thrilling days of yesteryear, when men wuz men, and some a' the women wuz just like men, too. Keep yer eyes closed tight while yew read this brochure, and picture yerself in old Deadwood. Pretend it's really that long-ago day when the famous Lena Larsson pulled into town on the afternoon stagecoach. Yep, it's happening right now. Bullets is zippin' and whizzin' ev'rywhere as our lady opens the door of the coach, and sees standin' there in the middle a' the fracas a tall, dark, long-haired gent by the name of Wild Bill Hiccup. Dramatic orchestral musik fills the air as Bill looks up. He sees the lovely Lena framed in the door of the coach, like a pikture in a big city art museum. A bullet bounces off his belt buckle.
>
> "Time out, Charley" he yells. "Yew too, Tex."

Wild Bill hisself!

Ole & Lena

The shootin' stops right kwick. Bill then holsters his pistols, combs his hair, and saunters over to the coach, actin' real casual.

"Hiccup's the name, ma'am," he sez politely as he helps her down. Bein' real suave he bows, and after spittin' away his chaw he kisses her hand. The lovely Lena responds with a coy smile.

"Larsson's mine," sez she with a giddy giggle.

Them words fairly explode inside Bill's head, turnin' his brain into a pound and a half of quiverin' lutefisk! Strains of violin musik fill the air. Yep, yew guessed it—it's love at first sight fer Wild Bill! In fact, once his keen marksman's eyes got focused in on Lena, his relationship with Calamity Jane wuz down the toilet.

Frum that moment on, Bill and Lena spend much a' their time hangin' out t'gether between gunfights. During them next months, he learned her how to chew and spit, and she learned him how t' play cards. Amongst the many fun games she taught him wuz Old Maid, Hearts, and Go Fish. Wild Bill loved those games, and he loved Lena too.

Of course, that didn't sit too flush with Calamity Jane. At first, she tried t' laugh it off, thinkin' it won't last. Then, after about 15 minutes she got all nervous, and finally she got downright bitter.

"That Larsson gal has got to go!" sez her. "It's she or me."

And so one cloudy noon, whilst Bill and Lena set loungin' in the Last Chance Saloon, dodgin' bullets and havin' some sips between spits, in walks Calamity lookin' mighty grim. And she's totin' two of ev'rything—two rifles, two shotguns, two Colt 45's, two tommyhawks—

"Front and center, yew dumb Norsky," she snarls, tossin' her whole arsenal onto the floor. "I'm challengin' yew to a duel!"

The saloon turns deathly silent, except fer the musik—which now sounds like the theme frum "Psycho"—and most a' the patrons exit kwickly through the back door. But Miss Larsson hangs tough. Slowly, she shoves back her chair, spits away her chaw, and—just to show she means bus'ness—she slips on her snowshoes (slowly, a' course), spurs and all. Then she slides down offa her chair (slowly), sidles slowly up to Calamity, and looks her square in her slow eye.

"I ain't afeared a' yew, dawg face," sez Lena with a (slow) drawl. "If yew want to fight, let it be here and now!"

The tension is so thick yew could cut it with a rusty razor.

"Okay, Norsky, ch-ch-choose yer weapons," sez Jane with a bit of a jitter, pointin' to the heap on the floor.

"Legs," sez Lena, kwick as a wink.

Jane blinks, and there's a moment of silence. "W-what caliber?" she finally responds, obviously flustered and not thinkin' too good.

Meanwhile, word a' the duel spreads all over town, and crowds of on-lookers begin to join the by-standers who is standin' by the saloon whilst they is lookin' on. Word is passed out to them that both women is now lyin' prone on the barroom floor.

"Dead?" asks a voice in the crowd.

"No, they's just gittin' ready t' spar," sez anuther.

The tension is thick. The musik stops. Two pale, white legs is thrust high in the air amid whistles and cat-calls.

"On three," cries the bar tender, who then begins the count. "One...Two..."

On the count of three, them hefty legs goes

blazin' into action! It's flesh locked on flesh—but mostly it's mind over matter in this stark moment a' truth. Lena gives it all she's got! Calamity gives it all she's got! And fer one brief moment, time stands still.

Then, suddenly, it's over! Lena launches Calamity high in the air, and like a well-thrown football she spirals right on through the large plate glass window out front, shattering them words that sez 'Last Chance Saloon' into about a gazillion pieces!

The crowd goes wild. Bill is ecstatic.

"Marry me, my sweet fresh heifer!" sez he between spits—and bein' all caught up in the spirit a' the moment, Lena blurts out them words which ev'ry man longs to hear...

"Yah, shure, yew betcha!"

Well, there's rejoicin' that day, the likes of which Deadwood ain't never heard. Wild Bill is celebratin' by holding shoot-outs ev'ry hour, on the hour—whilst the town's coroner is scurryin' about like a hungry weasel, buyin' drinks and passin' out price lists of his goods and services. It all lasts well past midnight.

But it seems that Lena's havin' second thoughts. She has trouble gittin' t' sleep that night, and towards mornin' she dreams of bein' married to Wild Bill. At first it's okay, but then—once she sees that brood of little long-haired kids spittin' all over the house and havin' gunfights in the parlor—she knows it won't work.

Alas, Deadwood's wedding bells never did chime fer Wild Bill and Little Lena. Our lady knew that in the long run, she couldn't never love no lightweight long-hair like Bill nohow. He'd have t' be triplets to weigh in at 444 pounds. And so the next day (which wuz a dark and gloomy one fer shure), Lena changed her answer frum *"Yah"* to...

"Nah."

After that, things wuz never the same betwixt them two frontier love-pups. By and by, Lena thunk it wuz best to move on—and after she'd left, Wild Bill became a downcast, morose man who did nuthin' but sit around and mope and spit and comb his hair. Then one day he turned to poker, and—well—yew know the rest a' that sad story.

As usual, the historians messed up and wrote Bill's name as "Hickok." But hey!—yew and I both know that ain't quite right.

Well, folks, that's the story in the brochure, and I'm shure them Deadwood Chamber folks would be more than happy to tell yew how accurate it is. Now I know yew'll want one a' them there colorful brochures fer yerself, as they's destined t' be hot collectibles. So next time yer passin' through Deadwood, be shure to stop in at the Chamber of Commerce and ask fer a copy.

And stand yer ground! If they play dumb, or say that they're fresh out, ask 'em to put yer name on a mailing list in case it ever gits reprinted.

Tell 'em yew'd like t' pass it on to yer children someday!

Lena Meets Pig's Eye Pete

Followin' her breakup with Wild Bill that summer, Lena snowshoed back east to Minnesoty, which fer some strange reason wuz called "the Gopher State," even though no one hadn't never seen no gophers there—at least not up 'til then yet.

So our lady settled down in the capitul city of St. Pawl then, near the Pig's Eye Dump *(which fer St. Pawl has got to be konsidered an upscale neighborhood)*. And there she took up housekeepin' in a overturned dumpster, which, as

Deadwood Chamber of Commerce
(Original Structure, now replaced)

Author's Note: I know that ev'ryone is real curious to know whut that Chamber a' Commerce looks like, and—well—this is the best I could do.

luck would have it, wuz not occupied at the time. She also got herself a really neat grocery kart, which wuz just the right size to hold all her belongings—so she got in her exercise by pushin' it around the neighborhood each day. And on one a' them daily walk-abouts, wouldn't yew know she met old "Pig's Eye Pete" hisself.

"So who the heck is Pig's Eye Pete?" yew ask. Well, if yew'da been up on things, yew'da already knowed that Pete shows up in Minnesoty hist'ry books as the infamous one-eyed French-Canadian Voyageur, Pierre Parrant. Now, most historians thunk Pete wuz long dead by this time, but the truth is that he most certainly warn't. He only looked like he wuz dead!

Sev'ral folks has queried me as to how Pete got his name. And I always points 'em to an old account, which describes his eye as—

> "blind, marble-hued, crooked, with a
> sinister white ring glaring around the
> pupil, giving a kind of piggish expres-
> sion to his sodden, low features."

Yet, whilst most on-lookers wuz rightly repelled by this double-ugly grizzled lookin' French hippie, Lena wuz strongly attracted to him, cuz he smelled kinda like 90 proof lutefisk. Moreover, Pete had fleshed out sideways somethin' awful in his downhill years, *until he weighed exactly 444 pounds!*

Now, before we trek on deeper into this here spell-binding story, let me tell yew somethin' more about Pete. In his younger days, the old sot had hisself a tavern down on the Missusippi, not far frum where the Pig's Eye Brew'ry now stands. It wuz kinduva lonesome spot back then. When he first set up shop, there warn't no other dawgs or folks livin' fer miles around.[6]

---

[6] Yew have to assume he wuz his own best customer.

Lena meets Pig's Eye Pete

That's why historians has chose to immortalize Ol' Pete by namin' him *the first white man ever to settle in the city of St. Pawl!* [7] And most a' them same historians will admit (off the record, a' course) that St. Pawl's lucky to be so well-represented, cuz the old coot wuz better lookin' than most a' the folks who's lived there ever since!

Anyways—yew kin see that Pete had t' be well along in years by the time that Lena showed up. The way I figure, he wuz easily on the downhill side of 97. Yet, he wuz remarkably well preserved—no doubt frum the vast amount a' spirits he'd consumed over the years. And whenever Lena saw Ol' Pete, she felt giddy as a first-year teenager.

"Oh heart be still!" sez Lena.[8] "Kan diss trooly be da man for who I haff saved myself all dese years?"

That heart wuz pumpin' somethin' awful, and the blood wuz sloshin' turbulently through Lena's veins, makin' her feel all gushy. She prayed that Pete wuz trooly the man of her dreams—even though he wuz old and ugly. Fer shure, he wuz the right weight—and he wuz bound t' be smarter than her, cuz ev'ryone wuz. Yet, Lena could not be shure he wuz "Mr. Right" until she'd learned if he could pass the most crucial test of all—beating her three outa four in leg wrestlin'.

Lena knew she'd have to find out—and right soon too, *whilst Pete's biological clock wuz still tickin'.*

[7] That is, assumin' he wuz white under all them layers of dirt.

[8] Apparently, Lena had this strange habit of speakin' to her body parts frum time to time.

Lena's Mysterious Dream

Lena's Mysterious Dream

But it wuz about this time, then, that Lena had a dream wherein she dreamed she saw the man of her dreams—*and it wuz not Pete!* He wuz—horror of horrors—a Swede, and a big one at that. Lena awoke at 3:00 AM in a cold sweat.

"Dat vas more uv a nightmare den a dream," she confided to friends the next day over a cup of egg coffee. "Da man vas flat broke and clumsy, vit tobaccy-stained teeth, and hair da kolor a' karrots!"

Even so, Lena could not shake the thought of this extraordinary man frum her brain. She tingled and broke out in large goosebumps whenever she thunk of him...

...cuz he too weighed exactly 444 pounds!

PART THREE:
OLE & LENA
GET TOGETHER

<u>Wedding Picture Of Ole And Lena</u>
Legends In Their Own Time

Ole & Lena

Chapter Six:
Ole And Lena In Minnesoty

(Preface To Part Three)

Well, yew all know that Ole and Lena will git together here in Part Three, which is the love story part. And yew've probubbly guessed that when they finally meet, it will be total dumb. Many stories has been writ on this topic over the years, some of which has been used as doktoral theses fer hist'ry majors at the University of Minnesoty.

Now, I'll be referrin' to some a' them theses here in Part Three. But we all know that college-writ theses is often a gnat shy in credibility, so I sorted 'em all into two piles—one of which is the "trustworthy" pile, and the other bein' the "untrustworthy" pile. And I'm only usin' those in the right hand pile, which is...uh...

Whatever.

Now This Here IS Part Three

Anyways, when we last saw Ole he wuz livin' on Snoose Boulevard in that glorious thrivin' heartland Minnesoty metropolis called Minneap'lis. And of course the lovely Lena wuz livin' at the Pig's Eye Dump, in the puny twin sister city of St. Pawl. It wuz predestined that Ole and Lena would meet. The only thing left to chance wuz *how* it would cum about.

A Night Out At The Bijou

The crucial cirkumstances that brought them two t'gether begun when Pig's Eye Pete took Lena by horse and buggy to Minneap'lis one Saturday night, fer the burlesque show at the Bijou Theater. And good golly wouldn't yew know that Ole wuz at the Bijou that same very night.[1]

Now, it just so happens that a few years ago, I had the unique opportoonity to interview Elijah Pitts—the last livin' person who wuz a eyewitness to this fateful event. Mr. Pitts wuz part of the large initial audience at the Bijou that night, and he wuz also one a' the 13 who survived the historic riot that followed—meanin' that (forchoonately fer us) he'd seen it all! Mr. Pitts turned 104 during that interview, and he died just two hours later.

The last word he uttered wuz *"Lena."*

Whut follows is a unedited transcript of a tape rekording that I made at the time—

Author: "Would yew please state yer full name?"

Mr. Pitts: "Are yew talkin' to me?"

Author: "Do yew see anyone else in this room?"

Mr. Pitts: "But yew already know my name!"

Author: "Dang it all! Askin' yer name is a formality, Sir. It's just fer the record!"

Mr. Pitts: "Well, I ain't puttin' up with no foolishness, sonny. Either yew want my story or yew don't. How much time yew think I got left, anyhow?"

---

[1] Author's note: There are several doktoral theses dealing with the reasons fer Ole bein' in the audience that night. Amung these, none are worth mentioning, except maybe Sören Kierkegaardson's 444 page paper entitled, <u>The Eschätölögicäl Meäning Underlying Unexpläined Resurgent Quäntum Events Observed ät the Bijou</u>. This reseärcher ättributed Ole's presence at the Bijöu tö mere chänce.

This here's the last picture ever uv Elijah Pitts, Aged 104

Author: "Okay, Mr. Pitts. Is it true that yew were in the audience at the Bijou theater on that fateful night?"

Mr. Pitts: "Of course I wuz, yew flea-brained idiot. I told yew that before! And like I said then, the place wuz packed t' the rafters that night, cuz Sally Randson wuz on the program. She always started out each show with her trained gopher act. But to tell the truth, us boys warn't much into exotic wild animals—except fer Sally herself *(heh heh)*. Yew see, it wuz her famous kootchie-kootchie fan dance whut brung us in. That gal had class to burn, and that dance a' hers had some real red-hot eyeball-poppin' moves, and some well-timed sexy jiggles, and...and...................."

Author: "Uh, Mr. Pitts?"

Mr. Pitts: "........................."

Author: "Mister PITTS!"

Mr. Pitts: "What?"

Author: "Yew were s'pposed to tell us about Ole and Lena."

Mr. Pitts: "Oh, uh...yes. Well, Lena wuz in the audience that night, and *she* wuz used to bein' the whole center of attenshun. Naturally, she wuz more than a mite jealous t' see us boys so glued on Sally, once she chucked them gophers *(heh heh)* and got to the fan dance part. Lena wuz sittin' there sulkin' and poutin' and thinkin' she'd like t' do somethin' about it, when she noticed there wuz somethin' real familiar about that dance.

"Vy, dat's yust anudder version uv da Lutefisk Stomp," she exclaimed, *"except fer da dumb fans!"*

Well, bein' as how Sally warn't doin' it quite right, Lena decided to show us all how the stomp wuz *really* s'pposed t' go. That's when she got up on stage, and that's why she started dancin' away.

Now, Sally could see right off that Lena wuz real good, and this made her dance all the harder. But no matter how hard she stomped, Lena did her one better. Sally danced so hard that her dainty little feet wuz like a blur to the naked...uh, naked.........
.................."

Author: "Mister Pitts?"

Mr. Pitts: "...eye! Then, Lena got out her snowshoes and put 'em on. That did it! *(Heh, heh)*. Lena now outstomped Sally frum one end a' the stage to the other, 'til the floorboards shook. And that's when Sally—desperate, and lookin' fer a way to redirect all them popped-out eyeballs which wuz now aimed straight at Lena—suddenly threw away her fans!

Well sonny, that crowd went flat-out berserk— and there followed an outrageous roof-raisin' ruckus, the likes a' which ain't never been matched in the whole hist'ry a' fan dancin'! Sally's cages of trained gophers wuz knocked over, and when they broke open, them cute little critters scattered in all directions.

Yew know, Minnesoty hadn't never had no gophers before then yet—at least not that I kin recall now though.[2]

---

[2] For a real good discussion on the genesis of gophers in Minnesoty, see The Origin of the Species, a 444 page paper by Darwin Rasmusson. Darwin considers alternate theories, but ultimately endorses the Bijou connection.

Anyways—yew already know that Ole wuz in the audience that night. But he'd not joined into that bedlam, bein's he wuz so awe-struck by the whole dang spectacle. And plus by golly he wuz bedazzled by the lovely Lena, who he knowed right off wuz the woman frum his dream.[3]

The chaos wuz fast approachin' Keystone Kop proportions when Lena spotted him spottin' her, and she sensed right off that he weighed exactly 444 pounds.[4] Lena stopped dead in her tracks—and as she gazed spellbound at Ole, he too gazed spellbound back at her. Why, it wuz love at first sight fer him, and ditto fer her—and it wuz bound to happen!

Meanwhile, the police raided the Bijou, and—after wrappin' Sally in a brown blanket like a big Pronto Pup—they hauled her off kickin' and screamin' to the city jail. Indeed, before things settled down that night, many a man wuz karted off t' that same jail...

...and they all went with smiles on their faces!"

Author's Note: At this point, Mr. Pitts took a one hour break fer his usual afternoon nap. Yew kin take one too, if yew like.

---

[3] Sigurd Freudson: <u>Dreams, And How They Are Shaped By Late Night Snacks</u>. In my opinion, the philosophical views set forth in this PG-13 rated paper are noteworthy fer a couple a' reasons, but I can't remember what they are. (444 pages of pretty dull reading)

[4] Author's note: For a provocative theory concerning the significance of the number 444, see <u>A Mathematical Theory of Prime Numbers As Applied To Fan Dancing</u>, by Alburt Einsteinson. This paper has been rated NC-17 (or wuz it $E=NC^2$-17) by the University of Minnesoty's Legion of Decency Censorship Board, and is available only at adult book stores on campus. (13 pages, with 444 pretty risque pictures)

Lena and Sally
on stage at the Bijou!

Showdown Time

Author: "Mr. Pitts?"

Mr. Pitts: (garbled)

Author: "MISTER PITTS!"

Mr. Pitts: "Huh?...What?"

Author: "Wake up, yew deaf old coot! Yer break's all done. I turned on the tape recorder again, and we're ready t' roll."

Mr. Pitts: "Oh—uh—yes. Where were we now?"

Author: "At the point where yew broke off, Ole and Lena had just met fer the first time."

Mr. Pitts: "Well, of course. I knew that! Yesiree, sonny. It wuz love at first sight! And even though the whole place wuz in absolute chaos, Lena had blanked it all out, she bein' faced with a new dilemma. She wuz now torn betwixt Big Ole and Ol' Pig's Eye Pete, both a' who wuz smarter than her and each a' who weighed exactly 444 pounds. Things bein' so equal in her head, it wuz the leg-wrestlin' that'd have t' be the tie-breaker.

Well, bein' such a impatient young lass, Lena had to have things settled right then and there. So she dragged Pete and Ole up onto the stage, which 4choonately did not collapse (remember that them two men totaled near half a ton whilst mingling). And to the delight of us 13 gents who wuz still there instead of off in jail with Sally, the leg wrestlin' commenced.[5]

---

[5] Author's note: For an unusual theory of the significance of the number 13, see Jesse Venturason: A Bizarre Applikation of the Random Occurrence of the Number 13 in Minnesoty Wrestling Matches to the Historikal Events That Have Shaped Our Predestined Destiny. (444 pages)

Ole & Pig's Eye shake hands before the leg wrestlin' matches

Pete's turn come first. All eyeballs wuz glued on the ol' sot, who looked kinda like a beached whale as he laid hisself down flat on the stage and gived it all he got. But when him and Lena squared off, the best he could do wuz two outa four. Then it wuz Ole's turn.

Now, yew will recall that Ole wuz skilled in the fine art of arm wrestlin', but hey—he wuz a durn good leg wrestler too! So when he and Lena locked legs up there on stage, shure enough Ole wins three outa four. All 13 survivin' spectators went wild, inkluding me! Fever-pitched palpitating pandemonium abounded, with wide-spread rootin' and tootin' and stompin' of feet. Of course, there'll always be some who argue that Lena woulda done better if she warn't wearin' her snowshoes. But hey—that plump little lassie wuz one happy puppy, who never once made no excuses fer her poor showin'.

Poor Pete, on the other hand, wuz crushed.

"I coulda done three outa four in my prime," Pete muttered. But Lena wuz as firm and tender as a chicken breast sandwich when she told him it wuz all over between 'em. The pooped old coot just slunk sorta slowly out the side door and sidled back t' St. Pawl. *And that's the last we hear of St. Pawl in this story!*

But before Pete left, he said, kinda cryptic-like, that he wuz goin' off t' share his down-time with his good friend, Jack Daniels.[6]

---

[6] Fer a scholarly dissertation concernin' attempts to establish the true identity of Jack Daniels through a search of the Ramsey County Federal Census Records, see Jim Beam's sprawling 444 page manuskript entitled, Using the Federal Census to Augment Historikal Accounts. Mr. Beam uses original plat maps of the area to show that, of the four Jack Daniels then residing in Ramsey County, one wuz livin' just 444 meters from the front door of Pig's Eye Pete's establishment, proving beyond all doubt that he could be the Mr. Daniels that Pete wuz referring to.

Author: "Well, Mr. Pitts, that wuz a most fascinating and informative account. Fer the first time, ev'ryone will know how Ole and Lena met, and..."

Mr. Pitts: "Hold on, sonny. I ain't done yet. In fact, I'm just gittin' to the good stuff! Do yew believe in trolls, sonny? Well, I didn't. But just as Ole wuz about to kiss Lena up there on stage fer the whole world to see, this burnt-lookin' little one-armed runt shows up, and then..."

Author's Note: Unforchoonately, my tape recorder malfunctioned at this point, and erased a part a' the tape. This left a gap, which has become famous as the *"17 missing minutes."* And that's a cryin' shame, becuz—like Mr. Pitts said—he wuz just gittin' to the good stuff. Things he told during those missin' minutes wuz so intense that it kept me right on the edge a' my chair fer the whole while—to say the least!

Anyways, I now resume the transcript at the point where the gap left off—

Mr. Pitts: "...and that about sums it up, sonny."

Author: "Thank yew Mr. Pitts, fer yer most informative story. I espeshully liked the last part."

Lena writin' to her Ma, while Ole catches sum Z-Z-Z's.

Ole And Lena Get Married

One month after the big bash at the Bijou, Lena penned the followin' letter to Norway (a better-than-average quality Xerox copy of this letter is on file at the Minnesoty Hysterical Society):

> "Dear Ma," *(it begins)*
> "I haff gone and met da most vunderful man! He veighs eggsactly 444 pounds. And he beat me tree outa fore in leg wrestlin' at da Bijou, so he iss eggsactly vut I alvays vanted. Need I say more? Ve got married last night, and now— since I got nuttin' bedder too do, I'm ketchin' up on all my letter-writing."
>
> Love, Lena.
>
> P.S. Two bad he's a Svede, but den yew kan't haff ev'ryting!"

At this point, we'll drop the curtain on this remarkable saga. I know I cut it kinda short at the end, but the full account of Ole and Lena's wedding and their married life t'gether is enough t' fill a <u>whole 'nother book</u>!

And I plan to write that book in the near future, by golly!

Until then, suffice it to say that Ole and Lena had 13 kids, and then each of their kids had 13 kids, and then— well—

Whatever.

So yew kin see that if yew happen to be in Minnesoty or any of them next-door states, and yew meet some folks who is of Norwegian or Swedish descent, chances are that there's a little bit of Ole and Lena in 'em. And if yer the least bit skeptical about that, just watch 'em fer a while or two, and I'm shure yew'll change yer mind.

Now, a' course yew know there's a whole heckuva lot more a' them "Ole and Lena" stories floatin' around. Summa them stories I couldn't use, cuz they wuz a bit blue—and this here is a wholesome book, writ fer readers of all ages. But most of 'em I couldn't use becuz they wuz undokumented—and of course this here is a first klass, fully dokumented hist'ry book, which I guarantee to be somewhere's up to 100% true.

In fact, here's a couple a' them "Ole and Lena" stories right now. I'm inkludin' 'em so's yew kin see the diff'rence between one that is dokumented and one that ain't.

First off, here's one frum Bill Johnson uv Minneap'lis, Minnesoty, who vouches that it's true—

> Ole n' Lena is havin' a nice quiet evening at home, when suddenly there's a knock at the door. Ole goes to answer, and—by golly—there's a sinister lookin' masked man pointin' a gun at him.
> "Yiminy Krickets!" sez Ole. "Are yew a robber?"
> "No, I'm a rapist!" replies the masked man.
> "Lena!" sez Ole, turnin' and callin' into the house. *"It's fer yew!"*

And then here's one frum Will Johnson uv St. Pawl, Minnesoty, who sez he could care less if it's true—

> Well—Ole wuz havin' a checkup at Doktor Peterson's office, and the good doktor noticed he's bin puttin' on weight.
> "Ole," sez the dok, "I want you to run ten miles a day for the next ten days. That'll help you shed some pounds."
> So Ole does just that, and it's exactly ten days later when he calls the doktor.
> "Dok," sez he, "I'm yust not too happy vit diss here veight loss program uv yers!"
> "So why is that, then, Ole?" asked Doktor Peterson. "Haven't you lost any weight yet?"

Ole & Lena with growing family
(Yew kin see that Lena's pregnant agin)

Author's comment about this picture:
Yew can see that Ole ain't nearly as big
as he wuz before he met Lena.
Married life does that to a man.

"Vell, a' course I did, Dok!" sez Ole. *"Da trouble iss— now I'm stuck out here vun hundred miles frum home!"*

So kin yew tell the diff'rence? It should be purty obvious. I'd be able to use Bill's stuff and not Will's, cuz Bill wuz able to vouch that it's true!

Anyways—if yew the reader has got any good stories, and yew kin vouch they're true, send 'em to me and just maybe I'll use 'em in the next book. And if I do, a' course I'd have to include yer name as bein' the source.

Until Next Time

So now (at last) in closing, let me say this. If yew just can't wait fer that next book, and yew really want to git t'gether personally and delve into some a' them there more "legendary" Ole and Lena tales *(that is to say, if yer standards ain't too high)*—yew'll just have t' stop in at my north woods cabin some dark and stormy indoor kind a' night. We'll find ourselves a nice warm spot in front a' the fireplace, and I'll pull up two of my most comfortable La-Z-Boy recliners. Then I'll cook up summa that there delicious egg coffee, while yew spread out a nice smorgasbord of all them tasty Danish and doughnuts *(which fer shure yew'd better remember to bring)*—followin' which we'll exchange tales, at the same time as we settle back to fill our stomachs.

Then—as Paul Harveyson says—we'll both know "the rest of the story."

Fer shure.

Yew betcha!

The End, by golly!

ORDER FORM: THE REMARKABLE SAGA OF OLE & LENA

Did you enjoy this book? Share it with others.

Qty	Title	Price	Total
	The Remarkable Saga of Ole & Lena	$10.95	
	Tax		
	Shipping & Handling		
	Total		

Name _____

Address _____

City/State/Zip _____

Telephone _____

Instructions:
- Minnesota residents add 6.5% sales tax ($.71 per book).
- Add $2.00 shipping & handling for first book, and .50 for each additional book.

- Make checks payable to Elliot House. Mail to:

> Elliot House
> 10030 - Elliot Ave. So.
> Bloomington, MN 55420